Mechanical Properties of Polymers and Composites

(IN TWO VOLUMES)

VOLUME 1

Mechanical Properties of Polymers and Composites

(IN TWO VOLUMES)

VOLUME 1

LAWRENCE E. NIELSEN
Monsanto Company
St. Louis, Missouri

MARCEL DEKKER, INC.   New York   1974

MARCEL DEKKER, INC.

305 East 45th Street, New York, New York 10017

LIBRARY OF CONGRESS CATALOG CARD NUMBER: 74-80758

ISBN: 0-8247-6183-9

Current printing (last digit);
10 9 8 7 6 5 4 3 2 1

PRINTED IN THE UNITED STATES OF AMERICA

To

Deanne

and

My Mother

CONTENTS

CONTENTS OF VOLUME 2

PREFACE

Polymers are relatively cheap, large volume structural
materials comparable in importance to metals. Their widespread
use and rapid growth result largely from their versatile
mechanical properties which cover the range from soft elastomers
to rigid materials. There is a need for a knowledge of mechanical properties of polymers by many groups of workers with widely
different backgrounds and interests. It has been about a
decade since an up to date book has been published on the
mechanical properties of polymers which is simple enough to be
easily understood by a scientist who is not a specialist in the
field but which has enough detail and depth to be useful for
those working with polymers. Many universities have established
departments in polymers or material sciences and are offering
more courses in polymer technology. This book, which includes
sections on problems, should be suitable for a one semester
course on mechanical properties of polymers. Much of the material in this book has already been tested in courses at Washing-
ton University. Industrial laboratories are putting more
emphasis on mechanical behavior and on applications involving
mechanical properties and less emphasis on synthesis of polymers
in recent years. Design engineers are being forced to gain
knowledge of viscoelasticity and the mechanical properties of

polymers as these newer materials displace metals and glass in more and more applications. Fabricators are becoming more aware of the importance of many factors (such as molecular weight, heat treatments, and molecular orientation, etc.) that affect the performance of their finished objects. Thus, there is a need for a book which discusses the mechanical properties of polymers at the elementary to intermediate level. It is the purpose of this book to fulfill the needs of all these people as far as the mechanical properties of polymers and composite materials are concerned.

This book outlines the general mechanical behavior of polymers to both environmental and structural factors. Environmental factors include time, temperature, external pressure, and magnitude of applied loads. Structural factors include molecular weight, branching, crosslinking, copolymerization, plasticization, crystallinity and crystallite morphology, molecular orientation, and block copolymerization. In all cases, emphasis is placed upon general principles, useful empirical rules, and practical equations. However, there is extensive reference also to the specific behavior of many common polymers. Developments, both experimental and theoretical, which have occurred in recent years are given the most attention.

Composite materials are now a major field of research and development activity. Composites are rapidly becoming important and useful structural materials, and probably the next major area for polymer applications is in the field of composite materials. A second objective of this book is to present a complete and unified picture of the mechanical properties

of composites in an easily understood manner. At present, no
comparable book exists which covers the entire field of the
mechanical behavior of composite materials, including par-
ticulate-filled polymers, fiber-filled materials, foams, and
high impact polymers and polyblends. Other books cover only
certain aspects of the field of composites or are too mathematical for most scientists and engineers who need a working knowledge of these materials. Many composite materials are entirely
different from materials used in the past because of their
anisotropy, that is, their mechanical properties may be entirely
different in different directions. For this reason, this book
discusses anisotropy in detail at an elementary level since most
scientists and engineers are familiar only with isotropic
materials.

Extensive reference is made to the literature. An attempt
has been made to select the most important references and those
that illustrate a point. Undoubtedly, a few important references
have been missed, but the author hopes he has performed a useful
service by culling out tens of thousands of references which
really add very little to our knowledge. Thus, for any given
topic, it should be easy for the reader to quickly acquaint
himself with what has been done by looking up the listed
references.

The author cannot acknowledge everyone who has helped in
the preparation of this book. Colleagues who have offered
numerous suggestions after reading the original manuscript
include Joseph Bergomi, Rolf Buchdahl, Melvin Hedrick, Myron Holm,

Allen Kenyon, James Kurz, Thomas Lewis, Eli Perry, and James
Woodbrey. Mrs. Bobbie Kaplan had the formidable task of typing
the manuscript. Deanne, my wife, not only helped with the proof
reading, the literature, and the indexes, but she tolerated the
author and his mass of papers for the three years required to
write this book.

                                        Lawrence E. Nielsen

Chapter 1

Mechanical Tests and Polymer Transitions

I. Introduction

Most plastic materials are used because they have desirable
mechanical properties at an economical cost. For this reason,
the mechanical properties may be considered the most important
of all the physical and chemical properties of high polymers for
most applications. Thus, everyone working with such materials
needs at least an elementary knowledge of their mechanical
behavior and how this behavior can be modified by the numerous
structural factors that can be varied in polymers. High polymers,
a few of which have their chemical structure shown in Appendix I,
have the widest variety and range of mechanical properties of all
known materials. Polymers vary from liquids and soft rubbers to
very hard and rigid solids. There are a great many structural
factors which determine the nature of the mechanical behavior of
such materials. One of the primary aims of this book will be to
show how the following structural factors, in addition to the
chemical composition, affect all of the major mechanical
properties of polymers:

1. Molecular weight
2. Crosslinking and branching
3. Crystallinity and crystal morphology
4. Copolymerization (random, block, and graft)

5. Plasticization
6. Molecular orientation
7. Fillers

In addition to the above structural and molecular factors, the following environmental or external variables are important in determining mechanical behavior:

1. Temperature

2. Time, frequency, or rate of stressing

3. Pressure

4. Stress and strain amplitude

5. Type of deformation (shear, tensile, biaxial, etc.)

6. Heat treatments or thermal history

7. Nature of surrounding atmosphere

There is a strong dependence on temperature and time of the properties of polymers compared to those of other materials such as metals. This strong dependence of properties on temperature and on how fast the material is deformed (time scale) is a result of the viscoelastic nature of polymers. Viscoelasticity implies behavior similar to both viscous liquids in which the rate of deformation is proportional to the applied force and to purely elastic solids in which the deformation is proportional to the applied force. In viscous systems all the work done on the system is dissipated as heat, whereas, in elastic systems all the work is stored as potential energy as in a stretched spring. It is this dual nature of polymers which makes their behavior so complex and at the same time so interesting. The great variety of mechanical tests and the numerous factors listed above would make the study of the mechanical properties of polymers very complex if it were not for some general phenomena and rules-of-thumb which greatly simplify the subject.

II. Mechanical Tests

    There are a bewildering number of mechanical tests and
testing instruments. Most of these tests are very specialized
and have not been officially recognized as standardized tests.
Some of these tests, however, have been standardized and are
described in the publications of the American Society for
Testing & Materials (1). Many of the important tests for plastics
are given as ASTM standards in a series of volumes. The important
volumes (parts) covering polymeric materials are listed in
Table 1. Although many tests have been standardized, it must be
recognized that a standardized test may be no better than one

Table 1

ASTM Standards

Part No.	Materials Covered
15	Paper, packaging
16	Structural sandwich constructions, wood, adhesives
20	Paint - Materials specifications and tests
21	Paint - Tests for formulated materials and applied coatings
24	Textiles - Yarns and fabrics
25	Textiles - Fibers
26	Plastics - Specifications
27	Plastics - Methods of testing
28	Rubbers
29	Electrical insulating materials

which is not considered as a standard. One objective of a
standardized test is to bring about simplicity and uniformity to
testing, and such tests are not necessarily the best for generating
the most basic information or the special type of information
required by a research problem. The tests may not even correlate
with practical use tests in some cases.

Besides the ASTM standard tests, a number of general
reference books have been published on testing and on the
mechanical properties of polymers and viscoelastic materials (2-7).
In addition to numerous tests, a great variety of units are used
in reporting values of mechanical tests. Stresses, moduli of
elasticity, and other properties are given in such units as
MKS (SI), cgs, and English units. A table of conversion factors
is given in Appendix II.

A. Creep Tests

Creep tests give extremely important practical information,
and, at the same time, give useful data to one interested in the
theory of the mechanical properties of materials. As illustrated
in Figure 1, in creep tests one measures over a period of time
the deformation brought about by a constant load or force. Most
creep tests measure the change in length of a specimen by a
constant tensile force, but creep tests in shear, torsion, or
compression also are made. If the material is very stiff and
brittle, creep tests often are made in flexure, but in such cases
the stress is not constant throughout the thickness of the
specimen even though the applied load is constant. Figure 2
illustrates these various types of creep tests. In a creep test
the deformation increases with time. If the strain is divided

by the applied stress, one obtains a quantity known as the
compliance. The compliance is a time-dependent reciprocal
modulus, and it will be denoted by the symbol J. (Some authors
use the symbol J for shear compliance and D for tensile compliance,
but this distinction will not be made here.)

   If the load is removed from a creep specimen after some
time, there is a tendency for the specimen to return to its
original length or shape. A recovery curve is thus obtained if
the deformation is plotted as a function of time after the
removal of the load.

   B. Stress Relaxation Tests

   In stress relaxation tests, the specimen is quickly
deformed a given amount, and the stress required to hold the
deformation constant is measured as a function of time. Such
a test is shown schematically in Figure 1. If the stress is
divided by the constant strain, a modulus which decreases with
time is obtained. Stress relaxation experiments are very
important for the theoretical understanding of viscoelastic
materials. Such tests, however, have not been as popular as creep
tests with experimentalists. There are probably at least two
reasons for this: 1. Stress relaxation experiments, especially on
rigid materials, are more difficult to make than creep tests.
2. Creep tests are generally more useful to engineers and designers.

   C. Stress-Strain Tests

   In stress-strain tests the buildup of force (or stress) is
measured as the specimen is being deformed at a constant rate.
This is illustrated in Figures 1 and 2. Occasionally stress-
strain tests are modified to measure the deformation of a specimen

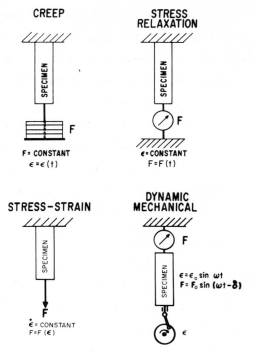

Fig. 1

Schematic diagrams of various kinds of tensile tests. F = force, ε = strain or elongation.

---

as the force is applied at a constant rate. Stress-strain tests have traditionally been the most popular and universally used of all mechanical tests, and are described by ASTM standard tests such as D638, D882, and D412. Unfortunately, these tests are more difficult to interpret than many other tests.

Figure 3 illustrates the great variation in stress-strain behavior of polymers as measured at a constant rate of strain. The scales on these graphs are not exact but are intended to give

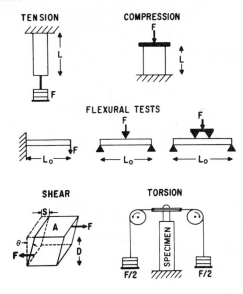

Fig. 2

Types of creep tests.

---

an order-of-magnitude indication of the values encountered. The
first graph (A) is for hard brittle materials. The second graph
(B) is typical of hard ductile polymers. The top curve in the
ductile polymer graph is for a material which shows uniform
extension. The lower curve in this graph has a yield point and
is typical of a material which cold-draws with necking down of the
cross section in a limited area of the specimen. Curves of the
third graph (C) are typical of elastomeric materials.

Figure 4 helps illustrate the terminology used for stress-
strain testing. The slope of the initial straight line portion
of the curve is the elastic modulus of the material. In a tensile

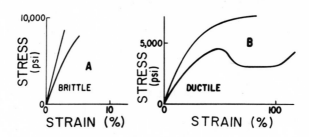

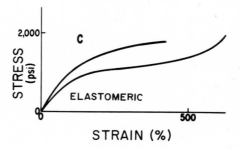

Fig. 3

General kinds of stress-strain curves.

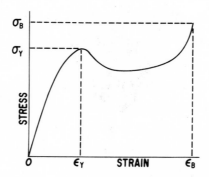

Fig. 4

Stress-strain notation.

test this modulus is Young's modulus,

$$E = \frac{d\sigma}{d\varepsilon} \; . \tag{1}$$

The maximum in the curve denotes the stress at yield σ_y and the elongation at yield ε_y. The end of the curve denotes the failure of the material, which is characterized by the tensile strength σ_B and the ultimate strain or elongation to break ε_B. These values are determined from a stress-strain curve while the actual experimental values are generally received as load-deformation curves. Thus, the experimental curves require a transformation of scales to obtain the desired stress-strain curves. This is accomplished by the following definitions:

For tensile tests:

$$\text{Stress } \sigma = \frac{\text{Force or load F}}{\text{Cross sectional area A}} \tag{2}$$

The strain ε can be defined in several ways as given in Table 2, but for engineering (and most theoretical) purposes, the strain for rigid materials is defined as

$$\varepsilon = \frac{L - L_o}{L_o} = \frac{\Delta L}{L_o} \; . \tag{3}$$

The original length of the specimen is L_o while its stretched length is L. At very small deformations, all the strains are equivalent. For shear tests (see Figure 2):

$$\text{Shear stress } \sigma_s = \frac{\text{shear force F}}{\text{area of shear face A}} \tag{4}$$

$$\text{Shear strain } \gamma = \frac{\text{Amount of shear displacement S}}{\text{Distance between shearing surfaces D}} = \tan \theta . \tag{5}$$

Table 2

Definitions of Strain

Definition	Name
$\varepsilon = \dfrac{L - L_o}{L_o} = \dfrac{\Delta L}{L_o}$	Cauchy (Engineering)
$\varepsilon = \dfrac{L - L_o}{L}$	
$\varepsilon = \ln(L/L_o)$	Hencky (True)
$\varepsilon = \dfrac{1}{3}\left[\dfrac{L}{L_o} - \left(\dfrac{L_o}{L}\right)^2 \right]$	Kinetic Theory of Rubber
$\varepsilon = \dfrac{1}{2}\left[\left(L/L_o\right)^2 - 1 \right]$	Kirchhoff
$\varepsilon = \dfrac{1}{2}\left[1 - \left(\dfrac{L_o}{L}\right)^2 \right]$	Murnaghan

If Hooke's law holds, the elastic moduli are defined by the following equations:

$$\sigma = E\varepsilon \quad \text{(Tensile tests)} \tag{6}$$

$$\sigma_s = G\gamma \quad \text{(Shear tests)} \tag{7}$$

E is Young's modulus, and G is the shear modulus.

Tensile stress-strain tests give another elastic constant called Poisson's ratio ν. Poisson's ratio is defined for very small elongations as the decrease in width of the specimen per unit width divided by the increase in length per unit length on the application of a tensile load:

$$\nu = \frac{-\varepsilon_T}{\varepsilon} = \frac{-d \ln \varepsilon_T}{d \ln \varepsilon} \,. \tag{8}$$

In this equation ε is the longitudinal strain while ε_T is the strain in the width direction or the direction perpendicular to the applied force. It can be shown that when Poisson's ratio is 0.50, the volume of the specimen remains constant while being stretched. This condition of constant volume holds for liquids and ideal rubbers. In general, there is an increase in volume, which is given by

$$\frac{\Delta V}{V_o} = (1 - 2\nu)\varepsilon \tag{9}$$

where ΔV is the increase in the initial volume V_o brought about by straining the specimen.

D. Dynamic Mechanical Tests

A fourth type of test is known as a dynamic mechanical test. Dynamic mechanical tests measure the response of a material to a sinusoidal or other periodic stress. Since the stress and strain are generally not in phase, two quantities can be determined - a modulus and a phase angle or a damping term. There many types of dynamic mechanical test instruments. One type is schematically illustrated in Figure 1. The general types of dynamic mechanical instruments are free vibrations, resonance forced vibration, nonresonance forced vibrations, and wave or pulse propagation instruments (3,4). Although any one instrument has a limited frequency range, the different types of apparatus are capable of covering the range from a fraction of a cycle per second up to millions of cycles per second. Most instruments measure either

shear or tensile properties, but instruments have been built to
measure bulk properties.

Dynamic mechanical tests, in general, give more information
about a material than other tests, although theoretically the
other types of mechanical tests can give the same information.
Dynamic tests over a wide temperature and frequency range are
especially sensitive to the chemical and physical structure of
plastics. Such tests are in many cases the most sensitive tests
known for studying glass transitions and secondary transitions in
polymers as well as the morphology of crystalline polymers.

Dynamic mechanical results are generally given in terms of
complex moduli or compliances (3,4). The notation will be
illustrated in terms of shear modulus G, but exactly analogous
notation holds for Young's modulus E. The complex moduli are
defined by

$$G^* = G' + iG'' \tag{10}$$

where G^* is the complex shear modulus, G' is the real part of the
modulus, G'' is the imaginary part of the modulus, and $i = \sqrt{-1}$.
G'' is called the loss modulus and is a damping or energy dissipation term. The angle which reflects the time lag between the
applied stress and strain is δ, and it is defined by a ratio
called the dissipation factor:

$$\tan \delta = G''/G'. \tag{11}$$

The tan δ is a damping term and is a measure of the ratio of
energy dissipated as heat to the maximum energy stored in the
material during one cycle of oscillation. For small to medium
damping, G' is the same as the shear modulus measured by other
methods at comparable time scales. The loss factor G'' is directly

proportional to the heat H dissipated per cycle as given by

$$H = \pi G'' \gamma_o^2 \qquad (12)$$

where γ_o is the maximum value of the shear strain during a cycle.
Other dynamic mechanical terms expressed by complex notation
include the complex compliance J* and the complex viscosity
η*.

$$J^* = J' - iJ'' \qquad (13)$$

$$\eta^* = \eta' - i\eta'' \qquad (14)$$

Some of the interrelationships between the complex quantities are:

$$G' = \omega \eta'' \text{ and } G'' = \omega \eta' \qquad (15)$$

$$G' = J'/J^2 \text{ and } J' = G'/G^2 \qquad (16)$$

$$\frac{G''}{G'} = \frac{J''}{J'} \qquad (17)$$

where

$$G^2 = G'^2 + G''^2 \qquad (18)$$

and ω is the frequency of the oscillations in radians per second.
Note that the real part of the complex viscosity is an energy
dissipation term similar to the imaginary part of the complex
modulus.

Damping is often expressed in terms of quantities conveniently
obtained with the type of instrument used. Since there are so
many kinds of instruments, there are many damping terms in common
usage such as the logarithmic decrement Δ, the half width of a
resonance peak, the half power width of a resonance peak, the Q
factor, specific damping capacity ψ, the resilience R, and
decibels of damping DB.

The logarithmic decrement Δ is a convenient damping term for

free vibration instruments such as the torsion pendulum illustrated
in Figure 5 for measuring shear modulus and damping. As shown in
the bottom of this figure, the successive amplitudes A_i decrease
because of the gradual dissipation of the elastic energy into heat.
The logarithmic decrement is defined by

$$\Delta = \ell n \, \frac{A_1}{A_2} = \ell n \, \frac{A_2}{A_3} = \cdots = \frac{1}{n} \, \ell n \, \frac{A_i}{A_{i+n}} \, . \qquad (19)$$

It is related to the dissipation factor approximately by

$$\Delta \doteq \pi \, \frac{G''}{G'} \qquad (20)$$

This equation is accurate at low damping ($\Delta < 1$), but the error
becomes large at high damping. More exact equations have been
discussed by Struik (8) and Nielsen (4). The standard ASTM test
is D2236-69.

Damping may be obtained from forced resonance vibration
instruments from plots of amplitude of vibration versus frequency
through the resonance peak. Figure 6 illustrates such a plot of
a resonance peak. Using the notation shown in this figure, the
damping may be expressed as

$$\frac{f_2 - f_1}{f_R} \doteq \sqrt{3} \, \frac{E''}{E'} \qquad (21)$$

or

$$\frac{f_2' - f_1'}{f_R} \doteq \frac{E''}{E'} \, . \qquad (22)$$

The damping is expressed in this case by E''/E' rather than as G''/G'
since in the case illustrated, Young's modulus is determined
instead of the shear modulus.

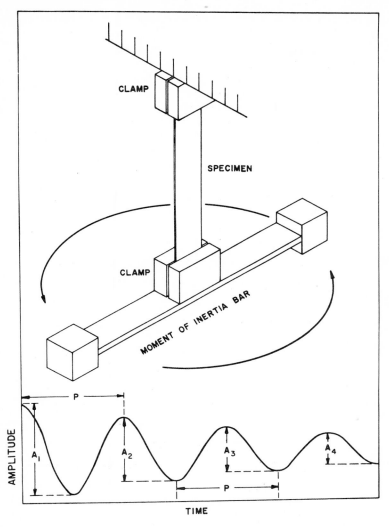

Fig. 5

Schematic diagram of a torsion pendulum and a typical damped
oscillation curve.   [Reprinted from L. E. Nielsen, SPE.J., <u>16</u>,
525 (1960).]

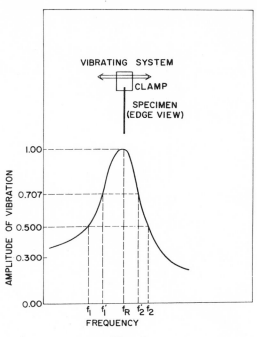

Fig. 6

Typical amplitude – frequency curve obtained with a vibrating
reed apparatus. [Reprinted from L. E. Nielsen, SPE.J., 16,
525 (1960).]

Other common damping terms may be expressed in terms of the
dissipation factor by the following equations:

$$Q^{-1} = \tan \delta = G''/G' \tag{23}$$

$$\psi = 2\pi \frac{G''}{G'} \tag{24}$$

$$R \doteq 1 - 2\Delta \doteq 1 - 2\pi \frac{G''}{G'} \tag{25}$$

$$DB = 20 \log_{10} \left(\frac{A_1}{A_2}\right) = \frac{20\Delta}{2.303} \doteq \frac{20\pi}{2.303} \frac{G''}{G'} \, . \tag{26}$$

Sometimes it is desirable to be able to estimate damping values in shear from measurements made in tension or visa versa. As a first approximation

$$\frac{E''}{E'} \cong \frac{G''}{G'} \, . \tag{27}$$

More exact equations such as

$$\frac{E''}{E'} = \frac{G''}{G'} \left[\frac{1}{1 + \frac{G'}{3B} \left[1 + (G''/G')^2 \right]} \right] \tag{28}$$

show that G"/G' is equal to or slightly greater than E"/E' (9,10). In equation (28), B is the bulk modulus.

    E. Other Tests

    There are many other types of mechanical tests in common usage. One of the most important of these tests is the impact strength of materials. Impact tests measure the resistance to breakage under specified conditions when the test specimen is struck at high velocity. Such tests are some measurement of the toughness of the polymer. They are very important practical tests but are difficult to define and analyze in scientific terms. The three most widely used impact testers are the falling ball or dart testers (4,5,11), Izod tester (12-14), and Charpy tester (12). High speed tensile stress-strain testers (15,16) also may be considered as impact or toughness testers. Another type of test which is replacing the conventional impact test to some extent is the fracture toughness test (17,18). Fracture toughness is a measure of the ability of a material to resist extension of a pre-existing crack.

Most plastics, except for a few thermoset materials, soften at some temperature. At the softening or heat distortion temperature, plastics become easily deformable and tend to lose their shape and quickly deform under a load. Above the heat distortion temperature rigid amorphous plastics become useless as structural materials. Thus, the heat distortion test, which defines the approximate upper temperature at which the material can be safely used, is an important test (4,5,7,19). As expected, for amorphous materials the heat distortion temperature is closely related to the glass transition temperature, but for highly crystalline polymers the heat distortion temperature is generally considerably higher than the glass transition temperature. Fillers also often raise the heat distortion test well above the glass transition temperature.

Other common mechanical tests include hardness, scratch resistance, friction, abrasion, tear, and fatigue tests (4,5).

III. Glass Transitions

Most polymers are either completely amorphous or have an amorphous-like component even if they are crystalline. Such materials are hard, rigid glasses below a fairly sharply defined temperature known as the glass transition temperature T_g. At temperatures above the glass transition temperature, at least at slow to moderate rates of deformation, the amorphous polymer is soft and flexible and is either an elastomer or a very viscous liquid. Mechanical properties show profound changes in the region of the glass transition. For instance, the elastic modulus may decrease by a factor of over 1000 times as the temperature is raised through the glass transition region. For this reason, T_g

can be considered the most important material characteristic of a
polymer as far as mechanical properties are concerned. Many
other physical properties change rapidly with temperature in the
glass transition region. These properties include coefficients
of thermal expansion (20,21), heat capacity (20,22), refractive
index (23), mechanical damping (4), nuclear magnetic resonance
behavior (24), and electrical properties (25-27). In view of
the great practical importance of the glass transition temperature,
a table of T_g values for many common polymers is given in
Appendix III. Elastomeric or rubbery materials have a T_g, or
a softening temperature, below room temperature. Brittle, rigid
polymers have a T_g above room temperature. Glass transitions
vary from -123°C for polydimethyl siloxane rubber to 100°C for
polystyrene and on up to above 300°C or above the decomposition
temperature for highly crosslinked phenol formaldehyde resins and
polyelectrolytes (28).

The glass transition temperature is generally measured by
experiments which correspond to a time scale of seconds or minutes.
If the experiments are done more rapidly so that the time scale
is shortened, the apparent T_g is raised. If the time scale is
lengthened to hours or days, the apparent T_g is lowered. Thus,
as generally measured, T_g is not a true constant but shifts with
time. Changing the time scale by a factor of ten times will shift
the apparent T_g by roughly 7°C for a typical polymer. The true
nature of the glass transition is not clear, and many conflicting
theories have been proposed (20, 29-35). Although the theoretical
nature of the glass transition is subject to debate, the practical
importance of T_g cannot be disputed.

A.   Chemical Structure and T_g

Several factors related to chemical structure are known to affect the glass transition temperature. The most important factor is chain stiffness or flexibility of the polymer. Long chain aliphatic groups, ether linkages, and CH_3 groups build

$$-\underset{\underset{CH_3}{|}}{\overset{\overset{CH_3}{|}}{Si}}-O-$$

flexibility into a polymer and lower T_g. The effect of the length of aliphatic side groups is illustrated by the methacrylate series (4,36):

Methacrylate Polymer	T_g (°C)
Methyl ester	105
Ethyl	65
n-Propyl	35
n-Butyl	21
n-Hexyl	-5
n-Octyl	-20
n-Dodecyl	-65

Rigid groups include substituted aromatic structures and pendant tertiary butyl groups; these relatively large and rigid groups raise the glass transition temperature. The effect of decreasing molecular flexibility by the substitution of bulky side groups onto a polymer chain is illustrated by the series: Polyethylene (T_g = -120°C), polypropylene (T_g = -10°C), polystyrene (T_g = 100°C), and poly(2,6 dichlorostyrene) (T_g = 167°C). However, it is the flexibility of the group, not its size, that is the factor

determining T_g. Thus, increasing the size of an aliphatic group
can actually lower the glass transition temperature as illustrated
in the above methacrylate series.

A second factor important in determining T_g is the molecular
polarity or the cohesive energy density of the polymer. Increasing
the polarity of a polymer increases its T_g. Thus, in the series:
Polypropylene (T_g = -10 °C), polyvinyl chloride (T_g = 85 °C), and
polyacrylonitrile (T_g = 101°C) the size of the side groups is
about the same, but the polarity increases. The effect of
cohesive energy density or the strength of intermolecular forces
is further illustrated by the series, poly(methyl acrylate)
(T_g = 3°C), poly(acrylic acid)(T_g = 106 °C), and poly(zinc arcylate)
(T_g > 400 °C)(28). In this series, the strong hydrogen bonds in
poly(acrylic acid) greatly increase the intermolecular forces
over those found in the methyl ester polymer. The intermolecular
forces are increased more in the zinc compound by the even stronger
ionic type of bonds which have many of the characteristics of
crosslinks.

A third factor influencing the value of T_g is backbone
symmetry, which affects the shape of the potential wells for bond
rotations. This effect is illustrated by the pairs of polymers:
Polypropylene (T_g = -10°) and polyisobutylene (T_g = -70°), and
polyvinyl chloride (T_g = 87°) and polyvinylidene chloride (T_g = -19°).
The symmetrical polymers have lower glass transition temperatures
than the unsymmetrical ones in spite of the extra side group.

The flexibility and cohesive energy density or polarity of
each group are nearly independent of the other groups in the
molecule to which they are attached (37-40). Because of this,

each group can be assigned an apparent T_{g_i} , and the T_g of a polymer becomes the sum of the contributions of all the groups, that is,

$$T_g = \sum_i T_{g_i} \, n_i \qquad\qquad (29)$$

where n_i is the mole fraction of group i in the polymer.

The strong dependence of T_g on free volume (or an equivalent factor) is shown by a simple empirical rule and by the pressure dependence of T_g. The empirical rule is (41,42):

$$(\alpha_\ell - \alpha_g) T_g \doteq 0.113 \pm 0.003 \qquad\qquad (30)$$

where α_ℓ and α_g are the volume coefficients of thermal expansion above and below T_g, respectively. Pressure increases T_g. O'Reilly (43) found that pressure increases the T_g of polyvinyl acetate at the rate of 0.022°C/atmosphere. The T_g of polyvinyl chloride increases 0.014°C/atmosphere while the rate of increase is 0.018°C/atmosphere for polymethyl methacrylate (44). For rubbers the rate of increase is about 0.017°C/bar (45), and for polypropylene it is 0.20°C/kg cm^{-2} (46). Theoretically, T_g should increase with pressure as a function of the ratio of the compressibility to the thermal coefficient of expansion of the polymer.

Most polymers show small secondary glass transitions below the main glass transition (4,47-49). These secondary transitions can be important in determining such properties as toughness and impact strength. These transitions will be discussed in more detail in later chapters.

B. Structural Factors Affecting T_g

The glass transition increases with number average molecular

weight $\bar{M}_n$ to a limiting asymptotic value of $T_g°$ for infinite
molecular weight.   In the practical range of molecular weights,
T_g is given by (32,33,50,51):

$$T_g = T_g° - K/\bar{M}_n \tag{30}$$

where K is a constant characteristic of each polymer. For
polystyrene $K \doteq 1.75 \times 10^5$, so its T_g increases from about 83°C
for a molecular weight of 10^4 to 100°C for infinite molecular
weight. The change in T_g arises from the ends of the polymer
chains, which have more free volume than the same number of atoms
in the middle of the chain.

Crosslinking increases the glass transition of a polymer by
introducing restrictions on the molecular motions of a chain (52-62).
Low degrees of crosslinking, such as found in normal vulcanized
rubbers, increase T_g only slightly above that of the uncrosslinked
polymer. However, in highly crosslinked materials such as phenol-
formaldehyde resins and epoxy resins, T_g is markedly increased by
crosslinking (54,57,59-62). Two effects must be considered:
1. The crosslinking per se.   2. A copolymer effect taking into
account that a crosslinking agent generally is not chemically
the same as the rest of the polymer (53). The chemical composition
changes as crosslinking increases, so the copolymer effect can
either raise or lower T_g.

Nielsen (4,58) averaged the data in the literature and
arrived at the approximate empirical equation

$$T_g - T_{go} \doteq \frac{3.9 \times 10^4}{M_c} . \tag{31}$$

The number average molecular weight between crosslinked points is M_c while T_{go} is the glass transition temperature of the uncrosslinked polymer having the same chemical composition as the crosslinked polymer, that is, $T_g - T_{go}$ is the shift in T_g due only to crosslinking after correcting for any copolymer effect of the crosslinking agent.

DiMarzio (63) and DiBenedetto (58,64) and others (59) have derived theoretical equations relating the shift in T_g caused by crosslinking. DiBenedetto's equation is

$$\frac{T_g - T_{go}}{T_{go}} \doteq \frac{KX_c}{1 - X_c} \doteq \frac{2K}{n_c} \,. \tag{32}$$

The mole fraction of the monomer units which are crosslinked in the polymer is X_c , and n_c is the number average number of atoms in the polymer backbone between crosslinks. The temperatures should be expressed in absolute degrees in this equation. The constant K is predicted to be between 1.0 and 1.2; it is a function of the ratio of segmental mobilities of crosslinked to uncrosslinked polymer units and the relative cohesive energy densities of crosslinked and uncrosslinked polymer (58). The theoretical equation is probably fairly good, but accurate tests of it are difficult because of the uncertainty in making the correction for the copolymer effect and because of errors in determining n_c .

The degree of crosslinking has been expressed by many different quantities. For vinyl type polymers where there are two backbone atoms per monomer unit,

$$\frac{X_c}{1 - X_c} \doteq \frac{2}{n_c} = \frac{M_o}{M_c} \,, \tag{33}$$

where M_o is the molecular weight of the monomer.

Plasticizers are low molecular weight liquids which lower the glass transition temperature of a polymer. A typical example is the use of dioctyl phthalate in polyvinyl chloride to convert the polymer from a rigid material to a soft flexible one. If the glass transitions of the two components A and B are known, an estimate can be made of the T_g of the mixture by one or the other of the equations:

$$T_g \doteq T_{gA} \, \phi_A + T_{gB} \, \phi_B \tag{34}$$

$$\frac{1}{T_g} \doteq \frac{W_A}{T_{gA}} + \frac{W_B}{T_{gB}} \tag{35}$$

The glass transition of the polymer is T_{gA} while that of the plasticizer is T_{gB}; the volume fraction of plasticizer is ϕ_B, and its weight fraction is W_B. Typical values of T_{gB} are between $-50°C$ and $-100°C$. In order to calculate more accurate values of T_g, additional information must be available such as the T_g of a known mixture or the coefficients of thermal expansion (α_A and α_B) of the pure components in both their liquid and glassy states (33,65). For each component i

$$\alpha_i = (\alpha_{\ell i} - \alpha_{g i}) \tag{36}$$

where $\alpha_{\ell i}$ is the volume coefficient of expansion above T_g, and $\alpha_{g i}$ is the coefficient below T_g. For most polymers $\alpha_A \doteq 4.8 \times 10^{-4}$ per °K. The T_g of plasticized polymers is then given by (33,66):

$$T_g = \frac{T_{gA} + \left(K\, T_{gB} - T_{gA} \right) \phi_B}{1 + (K-1)\phi_B} \tag{37}$$

where K is either an empirical constant or

$$K \doteq \alpha_B / \alpha_A \; . \tag{38}$$

Equation 37 becomes equation 34 if K = 1, and it is often close
to equation 35 if K = 2.

The glass transition temperatures of copolymers are very
analogous to those of plasticized materials if the comonomer B
is considered to be a plasticizer for homopolymer A. Equations
34, 35 and 37 are still applicable except that K is generally
assumed to be an empirical constant (33,66-68).

There is considerable confusion on how the glass transition
is affected by molecular orientation. In some experiments the
apparent T_g is lowered by orientation in the direction parallel
to the orientation (69-71). The T_g in direction perpendicular to
the orientation, on the other hand, may be increased (70). Others
find that orientation increases T_g (72,73). Still others find no
change of T_g with stretching of rubbers (74).

IV. Crystallinity

Many polymers are not completely amorphous but are more or
less crystalline. The degree of crystallinity and the morphology
of the crystalline material have profound effects on the mechanical
behavior of polymers, and since these factors can be varied over a
wide range, the mechanical properties of crystalline polymers take
on a bewildering array of possibilities. The degree of crystallinity
is generally measured by x-ray diffraction techniques (75,76) or by
measuring density (75,77), but some mechanical tests are the most
sensitive indicators of crystallinity (4). Morphological structure,
including length of chains between folds in crystals and spherulitic

structure, may be studied by light scattering (78, 79), small angle x-ray scattering (80), and electron microscopy (81).

Highly crystalline polymers such as polypropylene have a complex morphological structure. The polymer chains generally appear to fold into laminar structures of the order of 100 $\overset{\circ}{A}$ thick (81-85). Between the layers are amorphous-like chain folds and some chains which go from one layer to the next to tie the whole structure together. The lamellae often are part of a more complex spherulitic structure in which the lamellae radiate from a nucleation center (81, 85, 86). Slow growth of the crystallites and annealing emphasize spherulitic structure while quenching minimizes it. Figures 7 and 8 schematically illustrate some of the possible chain arrangements in crystalline polymers (87,88). The mechanical deformation behavior of such complex structures is varied and difficult to unambiguously unravel on a molecular or microscopic scale. In many respects the behavior of crystalline polymers is like that of two-phase systems as predicted by the older fringe-micelle model illustrated in Figure 7 in which there is a distinct crystalline phase imbedded in an amorphous phase (89). A long polymer chain can go through several crystallites and amorphous regions.

A. Melting Points

Crystalline polymers do not have sharp melting points. Part of the crystallites, which are small or imperfect, melt before the final melting point is reached. An equilibrium theory giving the degree of crystallinity as a function of temperature for crystallizable copolymers has been developed by Flory (90). A nonequilibrium theory which may be applicable for some quenched

Fig. 7

Fringed-micelle model of crystalline polymers. [Reprinted
from W. M. D. Bryant, J. Polym. Sci., 2, 547 (1947).]

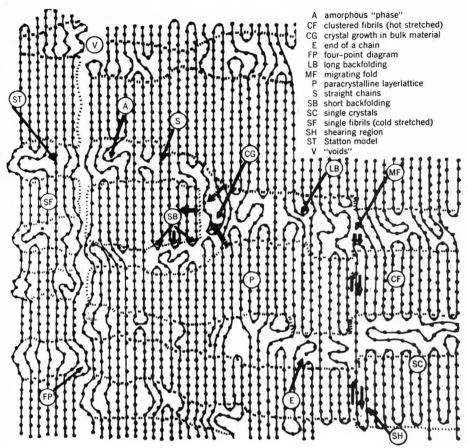

A   amorphous "phase"
CF clustered fibrils (hot stretched)
CG crystal growth in bulk material
E   end of a chain
FP four-point diagram
LB long backfolding
MF migrating fold
P   paracrystalline layerlattice
S   straight chains
SB short backfolding
SC single crystals
SF single fibrils (cold stretched)
SH shearing region
ST Statton model
V   "voids"

Fig. 8

Imperfect folded chain model of a single polymer crystal, which
makes up part of a spherulite. [Reprinted from R. Hosemann,
Polymer, 3, 349 (1962).]

polymers has been proposed by Wunderlich (91). In the crystallization of copolymers, the longest segments of the crystallizable
component crystallize first at the highest temperature. At lower

temperatures the shorter segments crystallize. This is expected
since low molecular weight homopolymers melt at lower temperatures
than high molecular weight material as given by (92,93)

$$\frac{1}{T_m} - \frac{1}{T_m^o} = \frac{2R \ M_o}{\Delta H_u \ \overline{M}_n} \ . \tag{39}$$

In this equation T_m is the melting point in degrees Kelvin of
polymer with a number average molecular weight $\overline{M}_n$. Polymer of
infinite molecular weight melts at T_m^o. The molecular weight of
the monomeric unit is M_o, R is the gas constant, and ΔH_u is the
heat of fusion per mole of crystalline polymer repeating unit.

Copolymerization usually lowers the melting point by
shortening of the length of crystallizable sequences. For random
copolymers the lowering of the melting point is (93):

$$\frac{1}{T_m} - \frac{1}{T_m^o} = \frac{-R}{\Delta H_u} \ \ell n \ X_A \tag{40}$$

where X_A is the mole fraction of the crystallizable comonomer A in
the copolymer. Solvents and plasticizers also lower the melting
point according to the equation (93-95):

$$\frac{1}{T_m} - \frac{1}{T_m^o} = \frac{R \ V_u}{\Delta H_u \ V_1} \ (\phi_1 - \chi_1 \ \phi_1^2) \ . \tag{41}$$

The molar volume of the polymer repeat unit is V_u, V_1 is the molar
volume of the solvent, ϕ_1 is the volume fraction of the solvent,
and χ_1 is an interaction term defining how good the solvent is for
the polymer. The term χ_1 is negative for very good solvents and
goes to about 0.55 for the limiting case of very poor solvents.
Good solvents lower the melting point more than poor solvents.

Appendix II lists the melting points of many common polymers.

More complete tables of melting points and heats of fusions may be found in references number 4, 36, 95 and 96.

Chemical structure factors affect both the melting point and the glass transition temperature in much the same manner. A good empirical rule for many polymers is (97-99):

$$\frac{T_g}{T_m} \doteq 2/3 \pm 0.04 \tag{42}$$

where the temperatures are given in degrees Kelvin. Symmetrical molecules such as polyvinylidene chloride tend to have ratios about 0.06 smaller than unsymmetrical molecules such as polypropylene.

V. Problems

1. Plot the various definitions of strain as defined in Table 2 as a function of $\Delta L/L_o$ from $\Delta L/L_o = 0$ to $\Delta L/L_o = 2$.

2. Polystyrene has a shear modulus of 1.25×10^{10} dynes/cm^2 and a Poisson's ratio of 0.35 at 25°C. What is its Young's modulus in pounds/sq.in. (psi)?

3. A rubber has a shear modulus of 10^7 dynes/cm^2. What is its modulus in the following units? (a) psi. (b) Newtons/m^2 (SI), (c) kg/cm^2.

4. A load of 100 pounds is applied to a specimen which has a length of 4 inches between grips, a width of 1 inch, and a thickness of 0.10 inches. If the Young's modulus of the material is 3.5×10^{10} dynes/cm^2, how much will the specimen elongate when the load is applied?

5. A parallel plate viscometer with a geometry such as shown in the lower left corner of Figure 2 is filled with a polymer melt of 10^4 poises. What force is required to move the plates parallel to one another at a velocity of 1 cm/sec if the spacing of the plates is 0.1 inch and their area is 1 square inch?

6. Derive the equation $(V - V_o)/V_o = (1 - 2\nu)\varepsilon$. V_o is the volume of the unstretched specimen.

7. What is the percent volume increase per percent elongation in a specimen when $\nu = 0.3$? When $\nu = 0$?

8. Plot $(T_g - T_{go})$ as a function of crosslinking using DiBenedetto's equation for poly(1,4-butadiene) and for polystyrene.

9. Plot T_g as a function of volume fraction of vinyl acetate for vinyl chloride-vinyl acetate copolymers using equations 34, 35, and 37, assuming that K = 2.

10. Homopolymer A melts at 200°C with a heat of fusion of 2000 calories/mole of repeat unit. What is the expected melting point of a random copolymer containing 10 molar percent of a comonomer B, which does not enter into the crystal lattice?

11. Toluene behaves as a plasticizer for polystyrene. Estimate T_g of a polystyrene containing 20 volume percent toluene.

VI. References

1. "ASTM Standards," American Society for Testing and Materials, 1916 Race St., Philadelphia, Pa.

2. T. Alfrey, Jr., Mechanical Behavior of High Polymers, Interscience, New York, 1948.

3. J. D. Ferry, Viscoelastic Properties of Polymers, 2nd Ed.,
    John Wiley, New York, 1970.

4. L. E. Nielsen, Mechanical Properties of Polymers,
    Van Nostrand Reinhold, New York, 1962.

5. J. V. Schmitz, Ed., Testing of Polymers, 4 vols., Interscience,
    New York, 1965 and later years.

6. A. V. Tobolsky, Properties and Structure of Polymers,
    John Wiley, New York, 1960.

7. R. Nitsche and K. A. Wolf, Ed., Struktur und Physikalisches
    Verhalten der Kunststoffe, Vol. 1 and 2, Springer-Verlag,
    Berlin, 1961 and 1962.

8. L. C. E. Struik, Rheol. Acta, 6, 119 (1967).

9. W. S. Cramer, J. Polym. Sci., 26, 57 (1957).

10. A. J. Staverman and F. Schwarzl, Die Physik der Hochpolymeren,
    Vol. 4, Chap. 1, H. A. Stuart, Ed., Springer-Verlag, Berlin, 1956.

11. ASTM standard falling dart impact test, D1709-67.

12. ASTM standard Izod impact test, D256-56.

13. D. Telfair and H. K. Nason, Modern Plastics, 20, 85 (July, 1943).

14. D. R. Morey, Ind. Eng. Chem., 37, 255 (1945).

15. ASTM standard high speed tensile tests, D1822-68 and D2289-69

16. S. Strella, High Speed Testing, Vol. 1, A. G. H. Dietz and
    F. R. Eirich. Ed., Interscience, New York, 1960. Also see
    articles in succeeding volumes of this yearly series.

17. G. R. Irwin, J. Appl. Mech., 61, A49 (1939).

18. S. Mostovoy and E. J. Ripling, J. Appl. Polym. Sci., 10,
    1351 (1966).

19. ASTM tests D648-56, D1525-65T, and D1637-61.

20. W. Kauzmann, Chem. Rev., 43, 219 (1948).

21. N. Bekkedahl, J. Res., Nat. Bur. Stds., 13, 411 (1934).

22. B. Ke, Newer Methods of Polymer Characterization,
    Interscience, New York, 1964.

23. R. H. Wiley and G. M. Brauer, J. Polym. Sci., 3, 647 (1948).

24. J. A. Sauer and A. E. Woodward, Rev. Mod. Phys., 32, 88 (1960).

25. R. M. Fuoss, J. Am. Chem. Soc., 63, 369 and 378 (1941).

26. T. H. Sutherland and B. L. Funt, J. Polym. Sci., 11, 177 (1953).

27. H. Thurn and F. Wuerstlin, Kolloid Zeit., 145, 133 (1956).

28. W. E. Fitzgerald and L. E. Nielsen, Proc. Royal Soc., A282,
     137 (1964).

29. R. F. Boyer and R. S. Spencer, Advances in Colloid Science,
     Vol. 2, p. 1, Interscience, New York, 1946.

30. J. H. Gibbs and E. A. DiMarzio, J. Chem. Phys., 28, 373 (1958).

31. M. Goldstein, J. Chem. Phys., 39, 3369 (1963).

32. T. G. Fox and P. J. Flory, J. Appl. Phys., 21, 581 (1950).

33. F. Bueche, Physical Properties of Polymers, Interscience,
     New York, 1962.

34. M. C. Shen and A. Eisenberg, Rubber Chem. Tech. (Rubber Reviews)
     43, 95 (1970).

35. A. Eisenberg and M. C. Shen, Rubber Chem. Tech. (Rubber Reviews)
     43, 156 (1970).

36. J. Brandrup and E. H. Immergut, Ed., Polymer Handbook,
     Interscience, New York, 1966.

37. R. A. Hayes, J. Appl. Polym. Sci., 5, 318 (1961).

38. W. A. Lee and J. H. Sewell, J. Appl. Polym. Sci., 12, 1397 (1968)

39. W. A. Lee, J. Polym. Sci, A2, 8, 555 (1970).

40. D. P. Wyman, J. Appl. Polym. Sci., 11, 1439 (1967).

41. R. Simha and R. F. Boyer, J. Chem. Phys., 37, 1003 (1962).

42. J. Moacanin and R. Simha, J. Chem. Phys., 45, 964 (1966).

43. J. M. O'Reilly, J. Polym. Sci., 57, 429 (1962).

44. P. Heydemann and H. D. Guicking, Kolloid Zeit., 193, 16 (1963).

45. M. S. Paterson, J. Appl. Phys., 35, 176 (1964).

46. E. Passaglia and G. M. Martin, J. Research, Nat. Bur. Stds.,
     68A, 273 (1964).

47. A. E. Woodward and J. A. Sauer, Adv. Polym. Sci., 1, 114 (1958).

48. R. F. Boyer, Polym. Eng. Sci., 8, 161 (1968).

49. J. A. Sauer, J. Polym. Sci., C32, 69 (1971).

50. T. G. Fox and P. J. Flory, J. Polym. Sci., 14, 315 (1954).

51. K. Ueberreiter and U. Rhode-Liebenau, Makromol. Chem., 49,
     164 (1961).

52. K. Ueberreiter and G. Kanig, J. Chem. Phys., 18, 399 (1950).

53. T. G. Fox and S. Loshaek, J. Polym. Sci., 15, 371, 391 (1955).

54. M. F. Drumm, C. W. H. Dodge, and L. E. Nielsen, Ind. Eng.
     Chem., 48, 76 (1956).

55. G. M. Martin and L. Mandelkern, J. Res., Nat. Bur. Std., 62,
     141 (1959).

56. H. D. Heinze, K. Schmieder, G. Schnell, and K. A. Wolf,
     Rubber Chem. Tech., 35, 776 (1962).

57. A. S. Kenyon and L. E. Nielsen, J. Macromol. Sci., A3, 275 (1969).

58. L. E. Nielsen, J. Macromol. Sci. - Revs. Macromol. Chem., C3,
     69 (1969).

59. Y. Diamant, S. Welner, and D. Katz, Polymer, 11, 498 (1970).

60. J. P. Bell, J. Appl. Polym. Sci., 14, 1901 (1970).

61. H. A. Flocke, Kunstst., 56, 328 (1966).

62. W. Fisch, W. Hofmann, and R. Schmid, J. Appl. Polym. Sci., 13,
     295 (1969).

63. E. A. DiMarzio, J. Res., Nat. Bur. Stds., 68A, 611 (1964).

64. A. T. DiBenedetto, unpublished private communication.

65. F. N. Kelley and F. Bueche, J. Polym. Sci., 14, 315 (1954).

66. M. Gordon and J. S. Taylor, J. Appl. Chem. (London), 2, 493 (1952).

67. L. A. Wood, J. Polym. Sci., 28, 319 (1958).

68. K. H. Illers, Zeit. Elektrochem., 70, 353 (1966).

69. L. E. Nielsen and R. Buchdahl, J. Appl. Phys., 21, 488 (1950).

70. K. E. Polmanter, J. A. Thorne, and J. D. Helmer, Rubber Chem.
     Tech., 39, 1403 (1966).

71. K. H. Hellwege, R. Kaiser, and K. Kuphal, Kolloid Zeit., 157 27 (1958).

72. W. O. Stratton, J. Poly. Sci., C20, 117 (1967).

73. G. Gee, P. N. Hartley, J. B. M. Herbert, and H. A. Lanceley, Polymer, 1, 365 (1960).

74. W. V. Johnston and M. Shen, J. Polym. Sci., A2, 7, 1983 (1969).

75. R. L. Miller, Encyclopedia of Polymer Science and Technology, Vol. 4, p. 449, Wiley, New York, 1966.

76. R. L. Miller, Crystalline Olefin Polymers, Part 1, p. 577, R. A. V. Raff and K. W. Doak, Ed., Interscience, New York, 1965.

77. F. P. Price, J. Chem. Phys., 19, 973 (1951).

78. M. B. Rhodes and R. S. Stein, J. Appl. Phys., 32, 2344 (1961).

79. R. S. Stein, Polym. Eng. Sci., 9, 320 (1969).

80. G. Porod, Advs. Polym. Sci., 2, #3, 363 (1961).

81. P. H. Geil, Polymer Single Crystals, Interscience, New York, 1963.

82. P. H. Till, J. Polym. Sci., 24, 301 (1957).

83. A. Keller, Phil. Mag., 2, 1171 (1957).

84. E. W. Fischer, Zeit. Naturforsch., 12A, 753 (1957).

85. P. Ingram and A. Peterlin, Encyclopedia of Polymer Science and Technology, Vol. 9, p. 204, Interscience, New York, 1968.

86. H. D. Keith and F. J. Padden, Jr., J. Polym. Sci., 41, 525 (1959).

87. W. M. D. Bryant, J. Polym. Sci., 2, 547 (1947).

88. R. Hoseman, Polymer, 3, 349 (1962).

89. K. Hermann, O. Gerngross, and W. Abitz, Zeit. Physik. Chem., B10, 371 (1930).

90. P. J. Flory, Trans. Faraday Soc., 51, 848 (1955).

91. B. Wunderlich, J. Chem. Phys., 29, 1395 (1958).

92. P. J. Flory, J. Chem. Phys., 13, 684 (1947) and 17, 223 (1949).

93. P. J. Flory, Principles of Polymer Chemistry, Chap. 13, Cornell University Press, Ithaca, 1953.

94. L. Mandelkern, Chem. Rev., 56, 903 (1956).

95. L. Mandelkern, Crystallization of Polymers, McGraw-Hill,
    New York, 1964.

96. R. L. Miller and L. E. Nielsen, J. Polym. Sci., 55, 643 (1961).

97. R. G. Beaman, J. Polym. Sci., 9, 470 (1952)

98. R. F. Boyer, J. Appl. Phys., 25, 825 (1954).

99. W. A. Lee and G. J. Knight, British Polym. J., 2, 73 (1970).

Chapter 2

Elastic Moduli

I. Isotropic and Anisotropic Materials

A. Isotropic Materials

Elastic moduli measure the resistance to deformation of materials when external forces are applied. Explicitly, moduli M are the ratio of applied stress σ to the resulting strain ε, i.e.,

$$M = \sigma/\varepsilon. \tag{1}$$

In general there are three kinds of moduli: Young's moduli E, shear moduli G, and bulk moduli B. The simplest of all materials are isotropic and homogeneous. Such materials have only one of each of the three kinds of moduli, and since the moduli are interrelated, only two moduli are enough to describe the elastic behavior of isotropic substances. For isotropic materials

$$E = 2G(1 + \nu) = 3B(1 - 2\nu) \tag{2}$$

where ν is Poisson's ratio. The distinguishing feature about isotropic elastic materials is that their properties are the same in all directions. Unoriented amorphous polymers and annealed glasses are examples of such materials.

B. Anisotropic Materials

Anisotropic materials have different properties in different directions (1-4). Examples include fibers, wood, oriented amorphous polymers, injection molded specimens, fiber-filled

composites, single crystals, and crystalline polymers in which
the crystalline phase is not randomly oriented. Thus, anisotropic
materials are really much more common than isotropic ones. But,
if the anisotropy is small, it is often neglected with possible
serious consequences. Anisotropic materials have far more than
two independent elastic moduli - generally a minimum of 5 or 6.
The exact number of independent moduli depends upon the symmetry
in the system (1-3). Theoreticians prefer to discuss moduli in
terms of a mathematical tensor which may have as many as 36
components, but engineers generally prefer to deal with the so-
called engineering moduli which are more realistic in most
practical situations. The engineering moduli can be expressed,
however, in terms of the tensor moduli or tensor compliances.
(See Appendix IV.)

A few examples of the moduli of systems with simple symmetry
will be discussed. Figure 1A illustrates one type of anisotropic
system known as uniaxial orthotropic. The lines in the figure
could represent oriented segments of polymer chains, or they
could be fibers in a composite material. This uniaxially oriented
system has 5 independent elastic moduli if the lines (or fibers)
are randomly spaced when viewed from the end. Uniaxial systems
have 6 moduli if the ends of the fibers are packed in some
pattern such as cubic or hexagonal packing. The 5 engineering
moduli are illustrated in Figure 1B for the case where the
packing of the elements is random as viewed through an end cross
section. There are now 2 Young's moduli, 2 shear moduli, and a
bulk modulus, in addition to 2 Poisson's ratios. The first
modulus E_L is called the longitudinal Young's modulus, whereas
the second one E_T is the transverse Young's modulus. The third

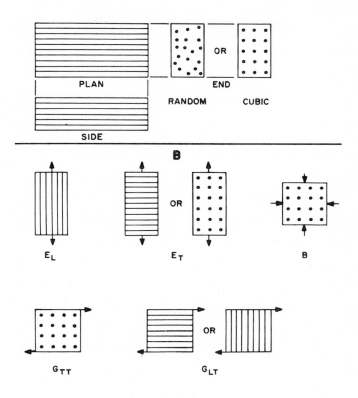

Fig. 1

A. Uniaxial oriented anisotropic material.

B. The elastic moduli of uniaxial oriented materials.

---

modulus G_{TT} is the transverse shear modulus, and the fourth one G_{LT} is the longitudinal shear modulus; this last modulus is also often called the longitudinal-transverse shear modulus. The 5th modulus is a bulk modulus B. The 5 independent elastic moduli could be expressed in other ways since the uniaxial system

now has at least 2 Poisson's ratios. One Poisson's ratio,
ν_{LT} , gives the transverse strain ε_T caused by an imposed strain
ε_L in the longitudinal direction. The second Poisson's ratio,
ν_{TL} , gives the longitudinal strain caused by a strain in the
transverse direction. Thus,

$$\nu_{LT} = \frac{-\varepsilon_T}{\varepsilon_L} \text{ for a longitudinal force; } \nu_{TL} = \frac{-\varepsilon_L}{\varepsilon_T} \text{ for a transverse (3) force}$$

where the numerators are the strains resulting from the imposed
strains which are given in the denominators.

The most common examples of uniaxially oriented materials
include fibers, films and sheets hot stretched in one direction,
and composites containing fibers all aligned in one direction.
Some injection molded objects are also primarily uniaxially
oriented, but most injection molded objects have a complex
anisotropy which varies from point to point and which is a
combination of uniaxial and biaxial orientation.

A second type of anisotropic system is the biaxially
oriented or planar random anisotropic system. This type of
material is schematically illustrated in Figure 2A. Four of the
5 independent elastic moduli are illustrated in Figure 2B; in
addition there are 2 Poisson's ratios. Typical biaxially
oriented materials are films which have been stretched in 2
directions, by either blowing or tentering operations, rolled
materials, and fiber-filled composites in which the fibers are
randomly oriented in a plane.

The mechanical properties of anisotropic materials will be
discussed in detail in following chapters on composite materials
and in sections on molecularly oriented polymers.

A

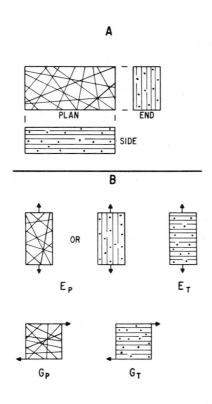

Fig. 2

A. Biaxial or planar random oriented material.

B. Four of the moduli of biaxial oriented materials.

II. Methods of Measuring Moduli

A. Young's Modulus

Numerous methods have been used to measure elastic moduli. Probably the most common test is the tensile stress-strain test (5-7). For isotropic materials, Young's modulus is

proportional to the initial slope of the stress-strain curve.
That is,

$$E = \frac{d\sigma}{d\varepsilon} = \frac{F/A}{(L - L_O)/L_O}$$ (4)

where F/A is the force per unit cross sectional area, L is the
specimen length when a tensile force F is applied, and L_O is the
unstretched length of the specimen. Equation 4 also applies to
anisotropic materials if the applied stress is parallel to one
of the principal axes of the material. The equation does not
give one of the basic moduli if the applied stress is at some
angle to one of the three principal axes of anisotropic materials.

Young's modulus often is measured by a flexural test. In
one such test a beam of rectangular cross section supported at
two points separated by a distance L_O is loaded at the midpoint
by a force F, as illustrated in Figure 2 of Chapter 1. The
resulting central deflection Y is measured with the Young's modulus
E calculated as follows:

$$E = \frac{FL_O^3}{4CD^3Y}$$ (5)

where C and D are the width and thickness of the specimen (8,9).
This flexure test often gives values of the Young's modulus
which are somewhat too high because plastic materials may not
perfectly obey the classical linear theory of mechanics upon
which equation 5 is based.

Young's modulus may be calculated from the flexure of other
kinds of beams. Examples are given in Table 1 (8,9). The table
also gives equations for calculating the maximum tensile stress
σ_{max} and the maximum elongation ε_{max}, which are found on the
surface at the center of the span for beams with two supports

Table 1

Young's Modulus from Flexure of Beams

Beam Geometry, Support, and Loading	E	σ_{max}	ε_{max}
1. Rectangular beam, center loaded, 2 supports.	$\dfrac{FL_o^3}{4CD^3Y}$	$\dfrac{3FL_o}{2CD^2}$	$\dfrac{6DY}{L_o^2}$
2. Rectangular beam, 2 supports, 2 equal loads $F/2$ at $L_o/4$ and $3L_o/4$.	$\dfrac{11FL_o^3}{64CD^3Y}$	$\dfrac{3FL_o}{4CD^2}$	$\dfrac{48DY}{11L_o^2}$
3. Rectangular cantilever beam fixed at one end with load at other end.	$\dfrac{4FL_o^3}{CD^3Y}$	$\dfrac{6FL_o}{CD^2}$	$\dfrac{3DY}{2L_o^2}$
4. Rod of diameter D with 2 supports, center loaded.	$\dfrac{4FL_o^3}{3\pi D^4Y}$	$\dfrac{8FL_o}{\pi D^3}$	$\dfrac{6DY}{L_o^2}$
5. Cantilever beam of circular cross-section fixed at one end with load at other end. D = diameter.	$\dfrac{64FL_o^3}{3\pi D^4Y}$	$\dfrac{32FL_o}{\pi D^3}$	$\dfrac{3DY}{2L_o^2}$

and at the point of support for cantilever beams. In these equations F is the applied force or load, Y is the deflection of the beam, D is the thickness of specimens having rectangular cross section or the diameter of specimens with a circular cross section.

Young's modulus may also be measured by a compression test.

(See Figure 2 of Chapter 1.)   The proper equation is:

$$E = \frac{\sigma}{\varepsilon} = \frac{F/A}{(L_O - L)/L_O} = \frac{F}{A} \ln \frac{L_O}{L} \tag{6}$$

Generally one would expect to get the same value of Young's modulus by either tensile or compression tests. However, it is often found that values measured in compression are somewhat higher than those measured in tension (10-12). Part of this difference may result from some of the assumptions made in deriving the equations not being fulfilled during actual experimental tests. For instance, friction from unlubricated specimen ends in compression tests results in higher values of Young's modulus. A second factor results from specimen flaws and imperfections which rapidly show up at very small strains in a tensile test as a reduction in Young's modulus. The effect of defects are minimized in compression tests.

In any kind of a stress-strain test the value of Young's modulus will depend upon the speed of testing or the rate of strain. The more rapid the test the higher is the modulus.

In a tensile stress relaxation test the strain is held constant, and the decrease in Young's modulus with time is measured by the decrease in stress. Thus, in stating a value of the modulus it is important to also give the time required to perform the test. In comparing one material with another the modulus values can be misleading unless each material was tested at comparable time scales.

In creep tests the compliance or inverse of Young's modulus is generally measured. However, Young's modulus can be determined from a tensile creep test since the compliance is the reciprocal of the modulus. While stress-strain tests are good for measuring moduli from very short times up to time scales of the order of seconds or minutes, creep and stress relaxation tests are best suited for times from about a second up to very long times such as hours or weeks.

Although creep and stress relaxation tests are most often measured in tension, they can be measured in shear (13-15), compression (16,17), flexure (13), or under biaxial stresses (18). They have even been measured in terms of volume changes which are related to bulk moduli (19-21).

B. Young's and Shear Moduli From Vibration Frequencies

The natural vibration frequency of plastic bars or specimens of various shapes can be used to determine Young's or shear modulus. Figure 3 illustrates four common modes of free oscillation. In Figure 3 (A and B) the effect of gravity can be eliminated for bars in which the width is greater than the thickness by turning the bar so that the width dimension is in the vertical direction. The equations for the Young's moduli

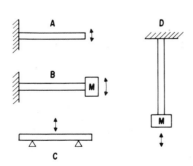

Fig. 3

Vibrating systems for measuring Young's modulus.

of the four cases illustrated in Figure 3 are given in Table 2
for the fundamental frequency. The shear modulus for the
natural torsional oscillations of rods of circular and rectangular
cross section also are given in Table 2 (22). Dimensions without subscripts are in centimeters; dimensions with the subscript
in are in inches. The moduli are given in dynes/cm^2. In the
table, R is the radius, μ is a shape factor given in Table 3
(5,23), C is the width, D is the thickness, ρ is the density of
the material making up the beam of total mass m, P is the period
of the oscillation, f_R is the frequency of the vibrations in
hertz or cycles per second, and I is the rotary moment of
inertia in g cm^2.

At high frequencies of 10^4 to 10^7 cycles per second Young's
modulus of fibers and film strips can be measured by wave
propogation techniques (24-29). An appropriate equation when
the damping is low is

$$E \doteq \rho v^2 \tag{7}$$

where v is the velocity of the ultrasonic wave in the material,
and ρ is its density.

III. Relation of Moduli to Molecular Structure

The modulus-temperature curve is basic to an understanding
of the mechanical behavior of polymers. It is possible to
predict much about the creep, stress-relaxation, and stress-
strain behavior from the modulus-temperature curve. This
modulus-temperature curve is also very sensitive to many
structural factors such as molecular weight, density of crosslinking, degree of crystallinity, copolymerization, plasticiza-

Table 2

Equations for Dynamic Moduli from Free and Resonance Vibrations

Method and Specimen	Modulus (Dynes/cm^2)
1. Torsion pendulum. Rectangular cross section.	$G' = \dfrac{64\pi^2 LI}{CD^3 \mu P^2} = \dfrac{38.54 IL_{in}}{C_{in} D_{in} \mu P^2}$
2. Torsion pendulum. Circular cross section.	$G' = \dfrac{8\pi LI}{R^4 P^2} = \dfrac{1.531 IL_{in}}{R_{in}^4 P^2}$
3. Vibrating cantilever reed. Rectangular cross section	$E' = \dfrac{38.24\rho L^4}{D^2} f_R^2$
4. Vibrating cantilever reed. Circular cross section.	$E' = \dfrac{16\pi^2 \rho L^4}{(1.875)^4 R^2} f_R^2$
5. Vibrating rectangular reed of mass m with mass M on end.	$E' = \dfrac{16\pi^2 (M+0.23m) L^3}{CD^3} f_R^2$
6. Free-free vibration of rod supported at nodal points. Circular cross section.	$E' = \dfrac{16\pi^2 \rho L^4 f_R^2}{(22.0)^2 R^2}$
7. Free-free vibration of rod supported at nodal points Rectangular cross section.	$E' = \dfrac{48\pi^2 \rho L^4 f_R^2}{(22.0)^2 D^2}$
8. Longitudinal vibrations of circular rod of mass m with large mass M on end.	$E' = \dfrac{4\pi L (M+m/3) f_R^2}{R^2}$
9. Longitudinal vibrations of rectangular rod of mass m with mass M on end.	$E' = \dfrac{4\pi^2 L (M+m/3) f_R^2}{CD}$

Table 3

Shape Factor μ

Width C Thickness D	μ
1.00	2.249
1.20	2.658
1.40	2.990
1.60	3.250
1.80	3.479
2.00	3.659
2.25	3.842
2.50	3.990
2.75	4.111
3.00	4.213
3.50	4.373
4.00	4.493
5.00	4.662
7.00	4.853
10.00	4.997
20.00	5.165
50.00	5.266
100.00	5.300
∞	5.333

$\mu \doteq 5.333 \ (1-0.63D/C)$ if $C/D > 2$.

tion, and phase separation which occurs in most polyblends.
This section will briefly summarize the effects of these factors
on the simplest of amorphous polymers. Actual polymers are
usually more complex in behavior than the generalized examples.
Later chapters will discuss more complex systems in detail.

A. Effect of Molecular Weight

Figure 4 shows the modulus-temperature curve for three
different molecular weights of an amorphous polymer such as
normal atactic polystyrene. If the time scale of the experimental
technique is about one second or longer, the drop in the modulus
of about three decades takes place near the glass transition
temperature of the polymer. If this drop in the modulus is
above room temperature, the material is a rigid polymer at room
temperature with a modulus of about 10^{10} dynes/cm^2. The

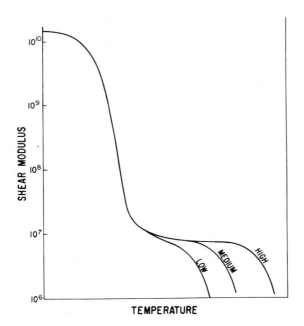

Fig. 4

Effect of molecular weight on the modulus-temperature curve
of amorphous polymers. Modulus is given in dynes/cm^2.

material is a viscous liquid or an elastomer if the big decrease
in modulus occurs below room temperature. Molecular weight has
practically no effect on the modulus below T_g. If the molecular
weight is high enough to be of interest for most applications
where mechanical properties are important, T_g and the drop in
modulus are also nearly independent of molecular weight. Except
at low molecular weights, only in the region above T_g is there
a strong dependence upon molecular weight. In the absence of
true crosslinks, the behavior is determined by molecular
entanglements (24,30-33). The higher the molecular weight the
higher must be the temperature before viscous flow becomes more
important than the rubber-like elasticity resulting from the
entanglements. Viscous flow occurs when a large fraction of
the entanglements move so as to relieve the stress on them
during the time scale of the experiment. The modulus takes
another drop from about 10^7 dynes/cm^2 when viscous flow dominates
the type of deformation of the polymer. Since a typical polymer
has a molecular weight of roughly 20,000 between entanglement
points, most molecules will have several entanglements, and the
number of entanglements will increase with molecular weight.
Thus, the length of the so-called rubbery plateau is a function
of the number of entanglements per molecule (34).

B.   Effect of Crosslinking

A small number of chemical crosslinks act about the same as
entanglements, but the crosslinks do not relax or become
ineffective at high temperatures. Thus, crosslinked elastomers
show rubber-like elasticity even at high temperatures and for
long times after being stretched or deformed. The modulus in
the rubbery region increases with the number of crosslinked

points or as the molecular weight between crosslinks M_c decreases. This behavior is illustrated in Figure 5. The modulus actually increases slightly with temperature as long as the kinetic theory of rubber elasticity is valid.

In addition to raising the modulus, crosslinking produces two other effects (35-37). First, when the crosslink density

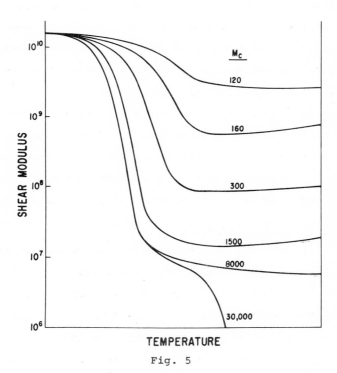

Fig. 5

Effect of crosslinking on the modulus-temperature curves of amorphous polymers. The numbers on the curves are approximate values of M_c. The value of 30,000 refers to an uncrosslinked polymer with a molecular weight of roughly 30,000 between entanglement points. Modulus units = dynes/cm^2

becomes fairly high, the glass transition temperature is
increased, so the drop in the modulus becomes shifted to higher
temperatures. Secondly, the transition region is broadened,
with the modulus dropping at a lower rate and plateauing at a
higher level. At least part of the broadening of the transition
region is due to the heterogeneity in the molecular weight
between crosslinks (36). Widely spaced crosslinks produce only
slight restrictions on molecular motions, so the T_g tends to be
close to that of the uncrosslinked polymer. As the crosslink
density is increased, molecular motion becomes more restricted,
and the T_g of the crosslinked polymer rises.

Below T_g, crosslinking has very little effect on the
modulus. Sometimes a slight increase is observed at very high
degrees of crosslinking. If perfect network structures could be
made, large increases in modulus should theoretically occur at
extremely high degrees of crosslinking such as in diamonds.

C. Effect of Crystallinity

Crystallinity in a polymer modifies the modulus curve of an
amorphous polymer above its T_g by at least two mechanisms (38-39).
First, the crystallites act as crosslinks by tying segments of
many molecules together. Secondly, the crystallites have very
high moduli compared to the rubbery amorphous parts, so they
behave as rigid fillers in an amorphous matrix. Thus, the
modulus increases very rapidly with the degree of crystallinity.
The effects of crystallinity are illustrated in Figure 6. The
crosslinking and filler effects of the crystallites last up to
the melting point. The melting point will generally increase
some as the degree of crystallinity increases. Above the melting
point, behavior typical of an amorphous polymer is found.

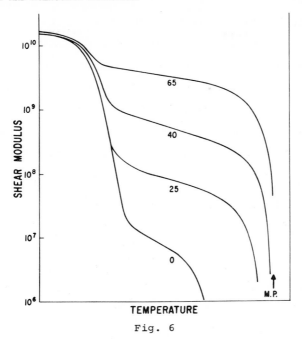

Fig. 6

Effect of crystallinity on the modulus-temperature curve.
The numbers on the curves are rough approximations of the
percent of crystallinity. Modulus units = dynes/cm^2.

Between T_g and the melting point, the moduli curves often have
an appreciable negative slope. This gradual change in modulus is
partly due to some melting of small or imperfect crystallites
below the melting point and partly due to a loosening of the
structure as a result of thermal expansion.

Below T_g, crystallinity has only a slight effect on the
modulus. This is because a glass has a modulus nearly as great
as that of an organic crystal (40). The intensity of the drop
due to the glass transition decreases with increasing degree
of crystallinity because the crystalline phase has no glass

transition. Crystallinity often has little if any effect on T_g,
but with some polymers crystallized under certain conditions,
T_g is raised (41,42). The increase appears to be caused by
either short amorphous segments between two crystallites or by
stresses put on the amorphous chain sequences as a result of the
crystallization process. Thus, quench cooling tends to increase
T_g while annealing reduces T_g back to the value typical of the
amorphous polymer.

D.   Copolymerization and Plasticization

Plasticizers and copolymerization shift the glass transition
temperature as discussed in Chapter 1. As a result, the basic
modulus-temperature curve is shifted as shown in Figure 7 for
different compositions; the shift in the modulus curve is
essentially the same as the shift in T_g.

Copolymers and plasticized materials often show another
effect - a broadening of the transition region with a decrease
in the slope of the modulus curve in the region of the inflection
point. This effect is most pronounced with plasticizers which
are poor solvents for the polymer (43-47). Heterogeneous
copolymers, in which there is a change in overall chemical
composition in going from one molecule to another, also have
broad transition regions (48-50). This heterogeneity can result
from the fact that in most copolymerizations the first polymer
formed tends to be richer in one component than the other, while
during the last part of the polymerization reaction the molecules
become richer in the other comonomer. This results in a mixture
with a distribution of glass transitions. Polymer mixtures of
different chemical composition tend to be insoluble in each other,

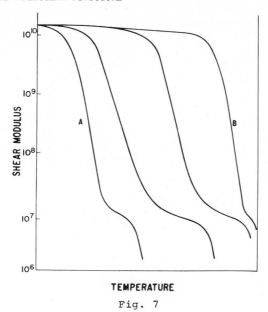

TEMPERATURE

Fig. 7

Effect of plasticization or copolymerization on the modulus-
temperature curve.   The curves correspond to different
plasticizer concentrations or to different copolymer
compositions. B is unplasticized homopolymer. A is either
a second homopolymer or plasticized B.

———————————————

and this tendency for phase separation is the cause of the
broadening of the transition region (50).   If the molecules of
different composition are completely soluble in one another and
if the mixture is homogeneous in the sense of being thoroughly
mixed, there is little if any broadening of the transition (51).

Plasticizers and copolymerization shift the glass transition
of the amorphous phase of crystalline polymers.   In addition,
the degree of crystallinity and melting point are lowered.   The

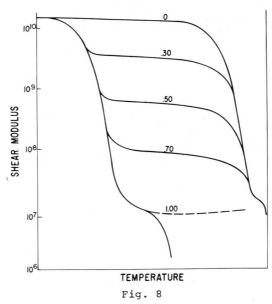

Fig. 8

Modulus-temperature curves of two-phase polyblends and block
polymers. The numbers on the curves are rough estimates
of the volume fraction of the component with the lower T_g,
which is shown both as an amorphous and as a crosslinked
material (dotted line). Modulus units - dynes/cm^2.

---

resulting effects on the modulus-temperature curves are as
expected from the previous discussion. There are also other
subtle effects which will be discussed in detail in later
chapters.

E. Block and Graft Polymers and Polyblends

   Except in the few cases where there is a close match of the
solubility parameters, mixtures of two polymers are insoluble
in one another and form two-phase systems (52-65). Block and
graft polymers, in which there are long sequences of each

homopolymer, also are two-phase systems (66-75). Thus, in block
and graft polymers there is the unique situation in which a
single molecule can be in two phases simultaneously. In two-
phase systems there are two glass transitions instead of the
usual one. Each transition is characteristic of one of the
homopolymers. The resulting modulus-temperature curve has two
steep drops as shown in Figure 8. The value of the modulus in
the plateau region between the two glass transitions depends
upon the ratio of the components and upon which phase tends to
be the continuous phase and which is the dispersed phase (65,76,77).

IV. Problems

1. What is the shear modulus of a polymer specimen as measured
    in a torsion pendulum with a period of 1.0 seconds if the
    specimen is 4 inches long, 0.40 inches wide, and 0.030 inches
    thick? The moment of inertia of the system is 5000 g cm^2.

2. What is the Young's modulus of the polymer in Problem 1 if
    Poisson's ratio is 0.35?

3. A nylon fiber has uniaxial orientation in which the polymer
    chains are parallel to the fiber axis. Is E_L greater than
    E_T? Is G_{TT} greater than G_{LT}? Why?

4. A beam of polystyrene is supported at each end. A load of
    10 pounds is applied to the middle. How much will the beam
    deflect if it is 1 foot long with a square cross section
    1 inch to the side? The Young's modulus is 3.5 x 10^{10} dynes/
    cm^2.

5. If the beam of problem 4 were a cantilever beam with the load
    on the end, what would the deflection of the end be?

6. A bar of polystyrene with a Young's modulus of 3.5×10^{10} dynes/cm^2 is dropped on the floor. As it rebounds into the air, it vibrates as a free-free beam. What is the frequency of the sound it emits if it is 8 inches long and has a diameter of 0.5 inches?

7. Although mixtures of most polymers form two-phase systems with two glass transitions, some mixtures do form one phase with a single T_g. An example of a single phase mixture is polyvinyl acetate ($T_g = 29°C$) and polymethyl acrylate ($T_g = 3°C$). What is the approximate T_g of a mixture containing equal volumes of the two polymers?

8. The modulus of a crystalline polymer changes from 1.3×10^{10} dynes/cm^2 below T_g to 10^9 dynes/cm^2 just above the glass transition region. What is the approximate degree of crystallinity? On raising the temperature to the region of the melting point, the modulus drops to 10^8 dynes/cm^2. What is the degree of crystallinity at this higher temperature?

9. Give several possible ways of telling the difference between an uncrosslinked polymer of very high molecular weight and one that has a very low degree of crosslinking.

10. Using only mechanical tests, how can a crystalline polymer be distinguished from a crosslinked one?

11. A glass fiber mat in which the fibers appear to be randomly oriented is impregnated with a thermosetting resin and cured. Strips are cut from the sheet in different directions, and their Young's modulus is measured. The Young's moduli are not the same in different directions. If the differences

are much greater than the expected experimental errors, what is the most probable cause of the difference in moduli?

12. A uniaxial composite consists of aligned glass fibers in a polymer matrix. If the modulus of the fibers is 20 times that of the polymer, is the longitudinal Young's modulus greater or less than the transverse Young's modulus? Is G_{LT} greater than G_{TT}?

13. A beam with a square cross section of thickness D is to be compared with a circular beam of diameter D. If the two beams of same length are supported on their ends and are center loaded with a weight W, which beam will deflect the most? What is the ratio of their center deflections if both beams have the same modulus?

14. Two beams of the same material are clamped at one end to form a cantilever beam. One beam has a square cross section of thickness D, and the other beam has a circular cross section of diameter D. The beams are set in vibration by a tap near the free end. If the length of the beams is the same, which beam will have the higher frequency of vibration? What is the ratio of their frequencies?

15. The Young's modulus of a polymer is to be measured by the frequency of vibration of a cantilever beam. The beam is 4 inches long, 0.5 inches wide, and 0.025 inches thick. The density of the polymer is 1.0. If the resonance frequency is 20 Hz, what is the Young's modulus?

V. References

1. R. F. Hearmon, Introduction to Applied Anisotropic Elasticity,
    Oxford University, 1961.

2. J. E. Ashton and J. M. Whitney, Theory of Laminated Plates,
    Technomic, Stamford, 1970.

3. J. F. Nye, Physical Properties of Crystals, Their
    Representation by Tensors and Matrices, Oxford University,
    1957.

4. I. M. Ward, Polymer Systems, Deformation and Flow,
    R. E. Wetton and R. W. Whorlow, Ed., Macmillan, London,
    1968, page 1.

5. L. E. Nielsen, "Mechanical Properties of Polymers,"
    Van Nostrand Reinhold, New York, 1962.

6. W. D. Harris, Testing of Polymers, Vol. 4, W. E. Brown, Ed.,
    Interscience, New York, 1969, p. 399.

7. ASTM Standards, D638, D882, and D412, Amer. Soc. for Testing
    and Materials, Philadelphia.

8. R. J. Roark, Formulas for Stress and Strain, 3rd Ed., McGraw-
    Hill, New York, 1954.

9. H. S. Loveless, Testing of Polymers, Vol. 2, J. V. Schmitz,
    Ed., Interscience, New York, 1966, p. 321.

10. Technical Data on Plastics, Manufact. Chem. Assoc.,
    Washington, D. C.

11. C. C. Hsiao and J. A. Sauer, ASTM Bull., #172, 29 (1951).

12. A. E. Moehlenpah, O. Ishai, and A. T. DiBenedetto,
    J. Appl. Polym. Sci., 13, 1231 (1969).

13. J. Marin and G. Cuff, Proc. ASTM, 49, 1158 (1949).

14. D. J. Plazek, _J. Colloid Sci._, 15, 50 (1960).

15. T. Yoshitomi, K. Nagamatsu, and K. Kosiyama, _J. Polym. Sci._,
     27, 335 (1958).

16. W. N. Findley, _Trans. Plast. Inst._, 30, 138 (1962).

17. D. G. O'Connor and W. N. Findley, _Trans. SPE_, 2, 273 (1962).

18. E. Z. Stowell and R. K. Gregory, _J. Appl. Mech._, 32E, 37
     (1965).

19. A. J. Kovacs, _Trans. Soc. Rheol._, 5, 285 (1961).

20. A. J. Kovacs, _Adv. Polym. Sci._, 3, 394 (1964).

21. W. N. Findley, R. M. Read, and D. Stern, _J. Appl. Mech._,
     34E, 895 (1967).

22. J. P. Den Hartog, _Mechanical Vibrations_, 4th Ed., McGraw-
     Hill, New York, 1956.

23. G. W. Trayer and H. W. March, _Nat. Advisory Comm. Aeronaut._,
     Report No. 334.

24. J. D. Ferry, _Viscoelastic Properties of Polymers_, 2nd Ed.,
     Wiley, New York, 1970.

25. H. A. Waterman, _Kolloid Zeit._, 192, 1, 9 (1963).

26. W. P. Mason and H. J. McSkimin, _Bell. Syst. Tech. J._, 31,
     #1, 121 (1952).

27. R. S. Witte, B. A. Mrowca, and E. Guth, _J. Appl. Phys._, 20,
     481 (1949).

28. A. W. Nolle, _J. Appl. Phys._, 19, 753 (1948).

29. B. A. Dunell and J. H. Dillon, _Textile Res. J._, 21, 393 (1951).

30. F. Bueche, _Physical Properties of Polymers_, Interscience,
     New York, 1962.

31.   G. C. Berry and T. G. Fox, Adv. Polymer Sci., 5, 261 (1968).

32.   T. G. Fox, S. Gratch, and S. Loshaek, Rheology, Vol. 1,
      Chap. 12, F. R. Eirich, Ed., Academic Press, New York,
      1956, p. 431.

33.   R. S. Porter and J. F. Johnson, Chem. Rev., 66, 1 (1966).

34.   G. V. Vinogradov, E. A. Dzyura, A. Ya. Malkin, and
      V. A. Grechanovskii, J. Polym. Sci., A2, 9, 1153 (1971).

35.   L. E. Nielsen, J. Macromol. Sci.-Revs. Macromol. Chem., C3,
      69 (1969).

36.   K. Ueberreiter and G. Kanig, J. Chem. Phys., 18, 399 (1950).

37.   A. V. Tobolsky, D. Katz, M. Takahashi, and R. Schaffhauser
      J. Polym. Sci., A2, 2749 (1964).

38.   L. E. Nielsen and F. D. Stockton, J. Polym. Sci., A1,
      1995 (1963).

39.   A. V. Tobolsky, J. Chem. Phys., 37 1139 (1962).

40.   J. J. Joseph, J. L. Kardos, and L. E. Nielsen, J. Appl.
      Polym. Sci., 12, 1151 (1968).

41.   D. W. Woods, Nature, 174, 753 (1954).

42.   S. Newman and W. P. Cox, J. Polym. Sci., 46, 29 (1960).

43.   L. E. Nielsen, R. Buchdahl, and R. Levreault, J. Appl. Phys.,
      20, 507 (1949).

44.   K. Wolf, Kunststoffe, 41, 89 (1951).

45.   K. Schmieder and K. Wolf, Kolloid Zeit., 127, 65 (1952).

46.   F. Linhardt, Kunststoffe, 53, 18 (1963).

47.   R. J. Hammond and J. L. Work, J. Polym. Sci., A1, 6, 73
      (1968).

48. L. E. Nielsen, _J. Am. Chem. Soc._, 75, 1435 (1953).

49. A. V. Tobolsky and I. L. Hopkins, _J. Polym. Sci._, Al, 7,
     2431 (1969).

50. G. Kraus and K. W. Rollmann, _Adv. In Chem. Series_, 99,
     189 (1971).

51. S. N. Chinai and L. E. Nielsen, _Mechanical Properties of_
     Polymers, Van Nostrand Reinhold, New York, 1962, p. 173.

52. A. Dobry and F. Boyer-Kawenoki, _J. Polym. Sci._, 2, 90 (1947).

53. R. Buchdahl and L. E. Nielsen, _J. Appl. Phys._ 21, 482
     (1950).

54. R. Ecker, _Rubber Chem. Tech._, 30, 200 (1957).

55. E. Jenckel and H. U. Herwig, _Kolloid Zeit._, 148, 57 (1956).

56. T. T. Jones, _British Plastics_, 33, 525 (1960).

57. G. Kraus, K. W. Rollman, J. T. Gruver, _Macromol._, 3, 92
     (1970).

58. G. Cigna, _J. Appl. Polym. Sci._, 14, 1781 (1970).

59. K. Fujimoto and N. Yoshimura, _Rubber Chem. Techn._, 41,
     1109 (1968).

60. S. Miyata and T. Hata, _Proc. 5th Inter. Congr. Rheology_,
     Vol. 3, S. Onogi, Ed.,Univ. Tokyo, Tokyo, 1970, p. 71.

61. K. Fujino, Y. Ogawa, and H. Kawai, _J. Appl. Polym. Sci._,
     8, 2147 (1964).

62. P. Zitek and J. Zelinger, _J. Polym. Sci._, Al, 6, 467 (1968).

63. S. G. Turley, _J. Polym. Sci._, Cl, 101 (1963).

64. P. Bauer, J. Hennig, and G. Schreyer, _Ang. Makromol. Chem._,
     11, 145 (1970).

65. M. Takayanagi, Memoirs Faculty of Eng., Kyushu Univ.,
     23, #1, 1 (1963).

66. J. A. Blanchette and L. E. Nielsen, J. Polym. Sci., 20,
     317 (1956).

67. E. B. Atkinson and R. F. Eagling, Physical Properties of
     Polymers, Soc. Chem. Ind. Monograph No. 5, Macmillan,
     New York, 1959, p. 197.

68. H. Hendus, K.-H. Illers, and E. Ropte, Kolloid Zeit.,
     216-217, 110 (1967).

69. G. Holden, E. T. Bishop, and N. R. Legge, J. Polym. Sci.,
     C26, 37 (1969).

70. G. M. Estes, S. L. Cooper, and A. V. Tobolsky, J. Macromol.
     Sci.-Rev. Macromol. Chem., C4, 313 (1970).

71. J. F. Beecher, L. Marker, R. D. Bradford, and S. L. Aggarwal,
     J. Polym. Sci., C26, 117 (1969).

72. E. Perry, J. Appl. Polym. Sci., 8, 2605 (1964).

73. M. Baer, J. Polym. Sci., A2, 417 (1964).

74. M. Buccaredda, E. Butta, and V. Frosini, J. Polym. Sci.,
     C4, 605 (1964).

75. R. J. Angelo, R. M. Ikeda, and M. L. Wallach, Polymer, 6,
     141 (1965).

76. L. E. Nielsen, Appl. Polym. Symp., No. 12, 249 (1969).

77. D. H. Kaelble, Trans. Soc. Rheol., 15, 235 (1971).

Chapter 3

Creep and Stress Relaxation

I. Introduction

Creep and stress relaxation tests measure the dimensional
stability of a material, and because the tests can be of long
duration, such tests are of great practical importance. Creep
measurements, especially, are of interest to engineers in any
application where the polymer must sustain loads for long times.
Creep and stress relaxation are also of major importance to
anyone interested in the theory of viscoelasticity.

For elastomeric materials, extremely simple equipment can
be used to measure creep or stress relaxation. For rigid
materials the measurements become more difficult, and more
elaborate equipment is generally required. In the creep of
rigid materials, the difficulty arises from the necessity to
measure accurately very small deformations and deformation rates.
In the case of the stress relaxation of rigid polymers, the
problem is to accurately measure the stress and the small strains
when the specimen is comparable in rigidity to that of the
apparatus, in which case small deformations in the apparatus or
slippage of the specimen in its grips can introduce very large
errors. A great many instruments have been described in the
literature. Instruments and techniques, along with many
references, have been described in detail by Ferry (1) and

Nielsen (2), so they will not be reviewed here.

Creep and stress relaxation tests are essentially the inverse of one another. Data from one kind of test can be used to calculate the other by fairly complex methods to be described later. However, to a first approximation the interconversion from creep to stress relaxation or vice versa is given by a simple equation (3):

$$\left(\frac{\varepsilon(t)}{\varepsilon_O}\right)_{creep} \doteq \left(\frac{\sigma_O}{\sigma(t)}\right)_{relax} \cdot \tag{1}$$

ε_O is the initial strain in a creep test while $\varepsilon(t)$ is the creep strain after time t. σ_O is the initial stress measured at the beginning of a stress relaxation test, and $\sigma(t)$ is the stress after time t.

II. Models

Very simple models can illustrate the general creep and stress relaxation behavior of polymers except that the time scales are greatly collapsed in the models compared to actual materials. In the models most of the interesting changes occur in about one decade of time, while polymers show the same total changes only over many decades of time.

A simple model for stress relaxation is a Maxwell unit, which consists of a Hookean spring and a Newtonian dashpot in series as shown in the insert in Figure 1. The modulus or stiffness of the spring is E, and the viscosity of the dashpot is η. In a stress relaxation experiment the model is given a definite strain ε while the stress σ is measured as a function of time. In the strained model, the change of the elongation of the spring is

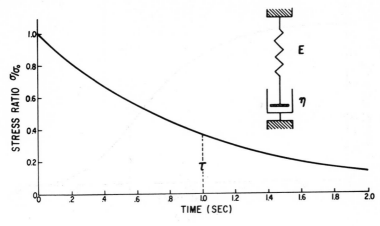

Fig. 1

Stress relaxation of a Maxwell model.   (Linear scales)

τ = 1 second.

_____

compensated by an equal change in the dashpot so that the net rate

of change is zero, that is,

$$\frac{d\varepsilon}{dt} = \frac{1}{E}\frac{d\sigma}{dt} + \frac{\sigma}{\eta} = 0 \qquad (2)$$

since $\varepsilon = \sigma/E$ for the spring and $\sigma/\eta = d\varepsilon/dt$ for the dashpot.

The solution of the above equation of motion is

$$\frac{\sigma}{\sigma_0} = e^{-\left(\frac{Et}{\eta}\right)} = e^{-t/\tau} \qquad (3)$$

where

$$\tau = \eta/E. \qquad (4)$$

The quantity τ is called the relaxation time.

Equation 3 is plotted with two different time scales in

Figures 1 and 2 for values somewhat typical of an elastomer.

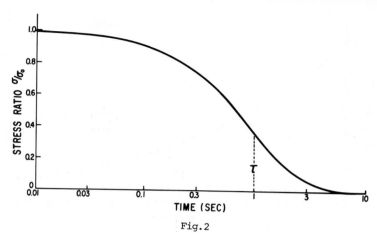

Fig.2

Stress relaxation of a Maxwell model on a logarithmic time scale.   Model is the same as Figure 1.

All the initial deformation takes place in the spring while at a later time the dashpot starts to relax and allows the spring to contract.   Most of the relaxation takes place within one decade of time on both sides of the relaxation time.   On the logarithmic time scale, the stress relaxation curve has a maximum slope and a stress ratio σ/σ_O of 0.3679 or e^{-1} at the time τ.   The stress relaxation may also be given in terms of a stress relaxation modulus $E_r(t)$.

$$E_r(t) = \sigma/\varepsilon = \frac{\sigma_O}{\varepsilon} e^{-t/\tau}$$ (5)

Creep behavior may be illustrated by the four-element model shown in Figure 3.   When a constant load is applied, the initial elongation comes from the single spring with the modulus E_1. Later elongation comes from the spring E_2 and dashpot η_2, in parallel, and from the dashpot with the viscosity η_3.   The total

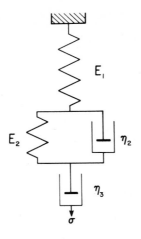

Fig. 3

A four-element model for creep.

---

elongation of the model is the sum of the individual elongations

of the three parts.   Thus,

$$\varepsilon = \frac{\sigma_O}{E_1} + \frac{\sigma_O}{E_2}\left(1 - e^{-t/\tau}\right) + \frac{\sigma_O}{\eta_3}\, t \tag{6}$$

where σ_O is the applied stress, and the retardation time τ is

defined by

$$\tau = \eta_2/E_2. \tag{7}$$

In a recovery test after all the load is removed at time t_1, the

creep is all recoverable except for the viscous part due to dash-

pot η_3.

The instant the load is removed there is a reduction in the

elongation of the model equal to σ_O/E_1.   The equation for subsequent creep recovery is:

$$\varepsilon = \varepsilon_2 \, e^{-(t-t_1)/\tau} + \frac{\sigma_0 t_1}{\eta_3} \qquad (8)$$

where

$$\varepsilon_2 = \frac{\sigma_0}{E_2} \left(1 - e^{-t_1/\tau} \right). \qquad (9)$$

Figure 4 illustrates the creep and recovery of a four element model with the following constants:

$\sigma_0 = 10^9$ dynes/cm^2 $E_1 = 5 \times 10^9$ dynes/cm^2

$\eta_2 = 5 \times 10^9$ poises $E_2 = 10^9$ dynes/cm^2

$\eta_3 = 5 \times 10^{11}$ poises $\tau = 5$ seconds.

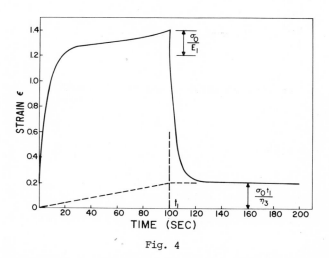

Fig. 4

Creep and creep recovery of a four-element model.

The creep experiment lasted 100 seconds, and then the load was removed for the recovery experiment.

Figures 5 and 6 show how the shape of the creep curve is modified by changes in the constants of the model. The value of the constants are given in Table 1. Curve I is the same as shown in Figure 4. Curve II shows only a small amount of viscous creep while in Curve III, viscous flow is a prominent part of the total creep. The same data were used in Figures 5 and 6, but notice the dramatic change in the shapes of the curves when a linear time scale is replaced by a logarithmic time scale. In the model, most of the recoverable creep occurs within about one decade of the retardation time.

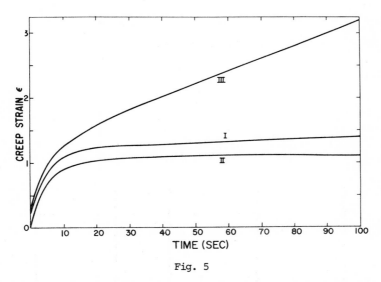

Fig. 5

Creep of a four-element model with the constants given in Table 1. Linear time scale.

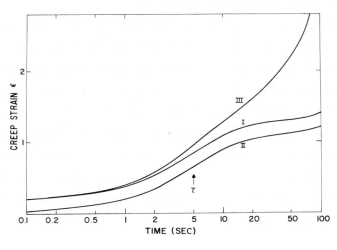

Fig. 6

Creep of a four-element model with the same constants as in
Figure 5 but with a logarithmic time scale.

Table 1

Constants for 4-Element Creep Model

Curve No.	E_1	η_3	E_2	η_2	σ_o
I	5×10^9	5×10^{11}	10^9	5×10^9	10^9
II	10^{11}	5×10^{11}	10^9	5×10^9	10^9
III	5×10^9	5×10^{10}	10^9	5×10^9	10^9

III. Distribution of Relaxation and Retardation Times

        In the previous section, models were discussed which had
only a single relaxation or retardation time. Actual polymers
have a large number of relaxation or retardation times distributed
over many decades of time. The distribution of retardation times
is designated as $L(\tau)$ while the distribution of relaxation times
is designated as $H(\tau)$.

        The distribution of retardation times $L(\tau)$ may be estimated
from the slope of a compliance curve $J(t)$ plotted on a logarithmic
time scale according to the equation

$$L(\tau) \doteq \frac{d[J(t)]}{d \ln t} \doteq \frac{1}{2.303} \frac{d[J(t)]}{d \log_{10} t} . \qquad (10)$$

If there is an appreciable viscous flow component to the creep,
it should be removed before making the calculation, so

$$L(\tau) \doteq \frac{1}{2.303} \frac{d[J(t) - t/\eta]}{d \log_{10} t} . \qquad (11)$$

Many more accurate and complex methods of estimating $L(\tau)$ have
been proposed. These methods have been summarized by various
authors including Leaderman (4) Ferry (1) and Tobolsky (5).

        The distribution of relaxation times $H(\tau)$ can be estimated
from a stress relaxation or $E_r(t)$ curve plotted on a log t
scale by

$$H(\tau) \doteq \frac{-d[E_r(t)]}{d \ln t} \doteq \frac{-1}{2.303} \frac{d[E_r(t)]}{d \log_{10} t} . \qquad (12)$$

More accurate but complex equations are discussed by Ferry (1)
and Tobolsky (5) among others.

In order to get accurate distributions of relaxation or retardation times, the experimental data should cover about ten or fifteen decades of time. It is extremely difficult to get experimental data covering such a great range of times at one temperature. Therefore, master curves (to be discussed later) have been developed which cover the required time scales by combining data at different temperatures through the use of time-temperature superposition principles.

Theoretically, distributions of relaxation or retardation times are useful and important because from such distributions other kinds of viscoelastic properties can be calculated. For instance, dynamic mechanical data can be estimated from stress relaxation data, or creep data can be calculated from stress relaxation results. Such calculations, however, are often complex. From the practical standpoint, very little use has been made of $L(\tau)$ and $H(\tau)$ in solving problems.

The above methods give continuous distributions of relaxation times. However, the molecular theories of viscoelasticity of polymers as developed by Rouse (6), Zimm (7), Bueche (8,9) and others (1, 10) give a discrete spectrum of relaxation times. A typical equation from these theories at temperatures above T_g is:

$$\tau_p = \frac{6\eta M}{\pi^2 \rho R T p^2} \quad , \quad p = 1,2,3 \ldots N/5 \tag{13}$$

The longest relaxation time τ_1 corresponds to $p = 1$. The important characteristics of the polymer are its steady state viscosity η at zero rate of shear, molecular weight M, and its density ρ at temperature T; R is the gas constant, and N is the

number of segments in the polymer chain. This equation only
holds for the longer relaxation times. The stress relaxation
curve can be approximated by

$$\frac{\sigma}{\sigma_o} \doteq \frac{5}{N} \sum_{p=1}^{N/5} e^{-t/\tau_p} \qquad\qquad (14)$$

IV. Superposition Principles

There are two superposition principles which are important
in the theory of viscoelasticity. The first of these is the
Boltzmann superposition principle, which describes the response
of a material to different loading histories (11). The second
is the time-temperature superposition principle or the W-L-F
equation, which describes the equivalence of time and temperature.

The Boltzmann superposition principle states that the
response of a material to a given load is independent of the
response of the material to any load which is already on the
material. Another consequence of this principle is that the
deformation of a specimen is directly proportional to the
applied stress when all deformations are compared at equivalent
times. The effect of different loads is additive.

For the case of creep, the Boltzmann superposition principle
may be expressed by

$$\varepsilon(t) = J(t)\,\sigma_o + J(t-t_1)(\sigma_1 - \sigma_o) + \dots + J(t-t_i)(\sigma_i - \sigma_{i-1})$$

$$(15).$$

The creep $\varepsilon(t)$ at time t depends upon the compliance function
$J(t)$, which is a characteristic of the polymer at a given
temperature, and upon the initial stress σ_o. At a later time t_1,

the load is changed to a value of σ_1. At still later times t_i, the load may be increased or decreased to σ_i. Figure 7 illustrates the Boltzmann superposition principle for a polymer which obeys a common type of behavior given by the Nutting equation (12,13):

$$\epsilon(t) = K \sigma t^n \qquad\qquad (16)$$

where K and n are constants which depend upon the temperature. The special case illustrated in Figure 7 is given by

$$\epsilon(t) = 10^{-5} \sigma t^{0.25} \qquad\qquad (17)$$

where σ has the units of pounds per square inch, and t is in

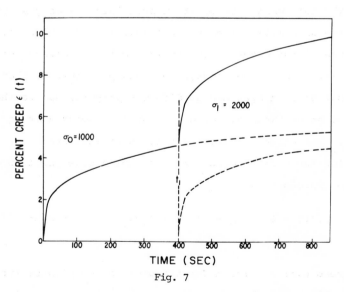

Fig. 7

Creep of a material which obeys the Boltzmann superposition principle. The load is doubled after 400 seconds.

seconds. Doubling the load after 400 seconds gives a total creep
which is the superposition of the original creep curve shifted
by 400 seconds on top of the extension of the original curve.

A similar superposition holds for stress relaxation
experiments in which the strain is changed during the course of
the experiments. The Boltzmann superposition principle for stress
relaxation is

$$\sigma(t) = E_r(t) \, \varepsilon_o + E_r(t-t_1)[(\varepsilon_1-\varepsilon_o)] + \cdots \qquad (18)$$

The initial strain ε_o is changed at time t_1 to ε_1.

Time-temperature superposition has been used for a long time;
early work has been reviewed by Leaderman (11). Creep curves
made at different temperatures were superposed by horizontal
shifts along a logarithmic time scale to give a single creep
curve covering a very large range of times. Such curves made by
superposition, using some temperature as a reference temperature,
cover times outside the range easily accessible by practical
experiments. The curve made by superposition is called a master
curve.

More recent advances in time-temperature superposition
principles have been made by Tobolsky (5,14) and by Williams,
Landel, and Ferry (1,15). The method of relating the horizontal
shifts along the log time scale to temperature changes as
developed by Williams, Landel, and Ferry is known as the W-L-F
method. The amount of horizontal shift of the time scale is
given by a_T. If the glass transition temperature is chosen as
the reference temperature, the shift factor for most amorphous

polymers is approximately:

$$\log_{10} \mathcal{Q}_T = \frac{17.44\,(T - T_g)}{51.6 + T - T_g} \tag{19}$$

where the temperatures are in degrees Kelvin. The shift factor $\mathcal{Q}_T$ is related to the change in viscosity η or the relaxation times τ by the relation

$$\log_{10} \mathcal{Q}_T = \log_{10}(t/t_o) = \log_{10}(\tau/\tau_o) \doteq \log_{10}(\eta/\eta_o). \tag{20}$$

A more exact relation is

$$a_T = \frac{\eta}{\eta_o} \; \frac{T_o \; \rho_o}{T\rho}. \tag{21}$$

The glass transition temperature T_g is often chosen as the reference temperature T_o; ρ and ρ_o are the density at temperature T and at the reference temperature T_o, respectively. At T_g, the viscosity is generally of the order of 10^{13} poises. The W-L-F equation holds between T_g and 100°C above T_g. If a temperature other than T_g is chosen as the reference temperature, an equation with the same form as equation 19 is obtained, but the numerical values change.

The temperature-time superposition principle is illustrated in Figure 8 by a hypothetical polymer with a T_g of 0°C for the case of stress relaxation. First, experimental stress relaxation curves are obtained at a series of temperatures over as great a time period as is convenient, say from 1 minute to 10^4 minutes (1 week) in the example in Figure 8. In making the master curve from the experimental data, the stress relaxation modulus $E_r(t)$ must first be multiplied by a small temperature correction factor $f(T)$. Above T_g this correction factor is T_g/T, where the

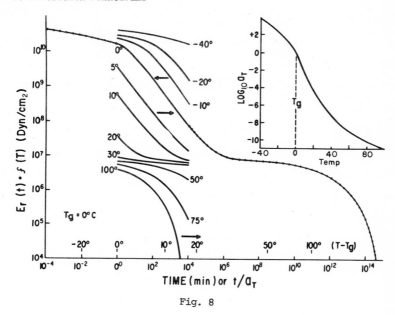

Fig. 8

W-L-F time-temperature superposition applied to stress
relaxation data obtained at several temperatures to obtain
a master curve. The master curve, made by shifting the
data along the horizontal axis by amounts shown in the insert
for a_T, is shown with circles on a line.

---

temperatures are in degrees Kelvin. This correction arises from
the kinetic theory of rubber elasticity, which will be discussed
later. Below T_g the W-L-F theory is not applicable, so a
different temperature correction should be used since the
modulus decreases with temperature below T_g but increases with
temperatures above T_g. Below T_g, it is often assumed that $f(T)=1$,
but McCrum (16,17) and Rusch (18) have suggested a more realistic,
but still small, correction. Next the corrected moduli curves
are plotted as the solid curves in Figure 8. The curve at some

temperature is chosen as the reference——T_g in the example.
The curves are then shifted one by one along the log time scale
until they superpose. Curves at temperatures above T_g are shifted
to the right while those below T_g are shifted to the left.   The
complete master curve is shown by the line with circles in
Figure 8; it covers 18 decades of time while the original data
only covered 4 decades.   For most amorphous polymers above T_g
the shift factor is given quite accurately by the W-L-F function
shown in the insert and in Table 2.   Thus, the stress relaxation
curve at 5°C should be shifted 1.427 decades in time to the
right (longer times) to properly superpose with the curve at 0°C.
The master curve has a prominent plateau near 10^7 dynes/cm^2;
this long plateau is characteristic of very high molecular weight

Table 2

W-L-F Shift Factors

$T-T_g$	Shift Factor, $\log_{10} a_T$
0	0
2	-0.6003
5	-1.4272
10	-2.6385
20	-4.5836
30	-6.0767
50	-8.2186
80	-10.251
100	-11.173

polymers and is due to chain entanglements, which act as temporary crosslinks. Since time and temperature are equivalent according to the superposition principle, the reduced time scale t/a_T can be replaced by a temperature scale. The equivalent temperature scale is shown above the reduced time scale on the abscissa of Figure 8 for a reference time of one minute.

Master curves are important since such curves are required to calculate the distribution of relaxation times as discussed earlier. Master curves can be made from stress relaxation data, dynamic mechanical data, or creep data. Figure 9 shows master curves for the compliance of poly(cis-isoprene) of different molecular weights. The master curves were constructed from the creep curves such as shown in Figure 10 (19). The reference temperature T_0 for the master curves was -30°C, which is about 43°C above T_g. The shift factors a_T follow the W-L-F theory, but since the reference temperature was not T_g, equation 19 does not hold. The W-L-F equation for this case is:

$$\log a_T = \frac{-8.20 \ (T - T_0)}{89.5 + T - T_0} \ .$$
(22)

Master curves often can be made for crystalline as well as for amorphous polymers (20-25). The horizontal shift factor, however, will generally not correspond to a W-L-F shift factor. In addition, a vertical shift factor is generally required which has a strong dependence upon temperature (23-25). At least part of the vertical shift factors result from the change in modulus because of the change in degree of crystallinity with temperature. Aging and heat treatments may also affect the shift

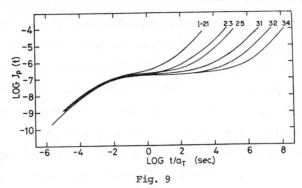

Fig. 9

Master curves for creep compliance of polyisoprene of different
molecular weights at a reference temperature of -30°C:

Curve Number	Mw
I-21	5.76×10^4
23	1.03×10^5
25	1.59×10^5
31	3.95×10^5
32	6.20×10^5
34	1.12×10^6

[Reprinted from Nemoto, et al., Macromol., 4, 215 (1971).]

factors. For these reasons, the vertical shift factors are
largely empirical with very little theoretical validity.

A few references to papers discussing master curves for the
creep and stress relaxation behavior of a number of polymers are
given in Table 3 (26-41).

V. Effect of Temperature

To a first approximation, the temperature dependence of
creep and stress relaxation can be predicted from the modulus-

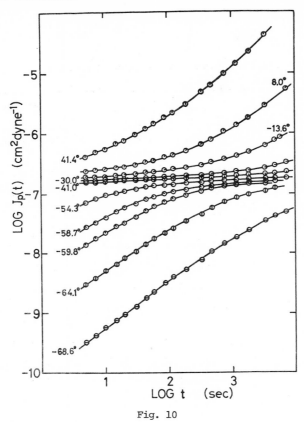

Fig. 10

Creep compliance of polyisoprene at different temperatures.
Data are for a fraction with a molecular weight of 1.12 x
10^6. [Reprinted from Nemoto, et al., <u>Macromol</u>., 4, 215
(1971).]

───────────────

temperature curve. This is illustrated for amorphous polymers
in Figures 11 and 12 where creep and stress relaxation curves are
shown at several temperatures corresponding to the different
parts of the modulus-temperature curve. Note that the

Table 3

Master Curves for Various Polymers

Reference Number	Test	Polymers
26	creep and stress relaxation	Polystyrene, polymethyl methacrylate, polymethyl acrylate
27	creep	Polystyrene
19	creep	Poly(cis-isoprene)
28	stress relaxation	SBD rubber
29	creep, stress relaxation, dynamic	Nylon 66
30	creep	Nylon 66
31	relaxation	Polymethyl methacrylate
32	relaxation	Polymethyl methacrylate and polymethyl acrylate
33	relaxation	Styrene-butadiene rubber
34	relaxation	Polyisobutylene, polymethyl methacrylate
14	relaxation	Polyisobutylene
35	creep and relaxation	ABS, styrene-acrylo-nitrile copolymer, polyvinyl chloride, polymethyl methacrylate
36	creep	Rubber
37	creep	Polycarbonate
25,38	relaxation	High density poly-ethylene
11	creep	Many materials
39	creep	Cellulose nitrate

Table 3

(Continued)

21	stress relaxation	Polyvinyl alcohol copolymers
24	stress relaxation	High density poly-ethylene
23	stress relaxation	Crystalline polymers
22	stress relaxation	Low density poly-ethylene
20	stress relaxation	Polypropylene, high and low density poly-ethylene
40	stress relaxation	Polycarbonate
41	stress relaxation	Polypropylene-vinyl chloride graft polymers

logarithmic scales are used for time, creep, and stress relaxation; the differences in the curves for the different temperatures would be more dramatic if linear scales were used. The creep or stress relaxation rates are low at low temperatures or for crosslinked polymers at temperatures well above T_g. The rates are high in the glass transition region and at temperatures above T_g for uncrosslinked polymers where viscous flow becomes important. If curves were given for more temperatures in Figures 11 and 12, the curves could be superposed to make a master curve.

VI.   Stress Dependence of Creep

If the Boltzmann superposition principle holds, the creep

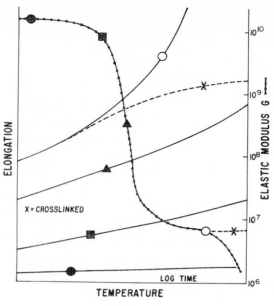

Fig. 11

Typical creep curves of amorphous polymers at different
temperatures. Symbols on the creep curves correspond to
temperatures which are shown on the superimposed modulus-
temperature curve (curve with small solid circles). The
creep curves are on a logarithmic time scale of about 3
decades.

---

strain is directly proportional to the stress at any given time.
That is, the creep compliance is independent of the stress. This
is generally true for small stresses, but the principle is not exact
for the large stresses encountered in practical structural
applications or for stresses approaching the fracture strength
of a polymer. In such cases, doubling the stress more than
doubles the amount of creep.

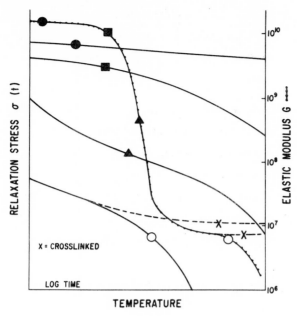

Fig. 12

Typical stress relaxation curves of amorphous polymers at
different temperatures. Symbols on the stress relaxation
curves correspond to temperatures which are shown on the
superimposed modulus-temperature curve (line with dots).

One way of describing this nonlinear behavior is by a power
law such as the Nutting equation (12,13):

$$\varepsilon = K \, \sigma^\beta \, t^n \tag{23}$$

where K, β, and n are constants at a given temperature. The
constant β is equal to or greater than 1.0. This equation
represents many experimental data reasonably accurately, but it
has received little theoretical justification (42-45).

The hyperbolic sine function also fits many experimental data, and it has considerable theoretical foundation (46-57):

$$\varepsilon = K(t)\sinh(\sigma/\sigma_c).$$ (24)

$K(t)$ is the function defining the time dependence of the creep. The constant σ_c is a critical stress characteristic of the material, and at stresses greater than σ_c the creep compliance increases rapidly with stress. Figure 13 illustrates the creep dependence of a polyethylene with a density of 0.950 at 22°C (58). In this case the critical stress σ_c was about 620 psi, and the creep was measured after 10 minutes. For this polyethylene the

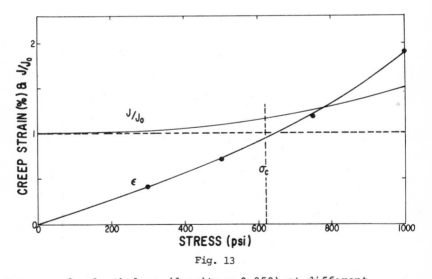

Fig. 13

Creep ε of polyethylene (density = 0.950) at different loads after 10 minutes, and J/J_0 as a function of applied stress. Deviation from the value of 1.0 indicates a dependence of creep compliance on load.

experimental data after 10 minutes are accurately given by:

$$\varepsilon = 0.792 \sinh (\sigma/620) \tag{25}$$

where the strain is given in percent and the stress is in psi.
Similar equations hold for other times and temperatures. Also
plotted in the same figure is the quantity

$$J/J_o = \frac{\sinh(\sigma/\sigma_c)}{\sigma/\sigma_c} \tag{26}$$

where J_o is the creep compliance at very low loads. This ratio
is 1.0 if the Boltzmann superposition holds. In the case of
polyethylene, deviations become apparent at about 200 psi, and at
a stress of 1000 psi, the compliance ratio J/J_o has increased
by 50 percent. In practical situations where a plastic object
must be subjected to loads for long periods of time without
excessive deformation, the stress should be less than the
critical stress σ_c.

Little is known about the variation of the critical stress
σ_c with structure and temperature. For the polyethylene
discussed above, σ_c decreased from 620 psi at 22°C to 390 psi
at 60°C; this appears to be a general trend with all polymers.
Turner (53) found that the value of σ_c for polyethylenes
increased by a factor of about five in going from a polymer
with a density of 0.920 to a highly crystalline one with a
density of 0.980. Reid (49,50) has suggested that for rigid
amorphous polymers, σ_c should be proportional to (T_g-T). For
brittle polymers, the value of σ_c may be related to the onset
of crazing.

Equation 24 implies that an applied stress does not shift

the distribution of retardation times. The shape of the curves
is not changed by stresses, and the curves could be superimposed
by multiplying the compliance by a constant for each stress to
bring about a normalization in the vertical direction. However,
in some cases (often rigid polymers at high loads) stresses do
change the distribution of retardation times to shorter times
(30,59-62). Then a horizontal shift is required on log time
plots to superimpose creep curves obtained at different stresses
even if the temperature is held constant.

Many other data in the literature show a strong dependence
of creep compliance on the applied load, although in some cases
the authors did not discuss this aspect of creep. Stress
dependence is found with all kinds of plastics. For instance,
the creep of polyethylene has been studied by several authors
(43,44,52,53,58,63-65), and so has rigid polyvinyl chloride
(49,50,52,60,62,66,67). Leaderman (68) studied plasticized
polyvinyl chloride. Polystyrene has been investigated by
Sauer (42,69), and ABS polymers have been studied also (56,62,70).
Polypropylene has also been a popular polymer (61,71,72). Sharma
studied a chlorinated polyether (Penton)(73) and cellulose
acetate butyrate (45). Nylon was studied by Catsiff, et al. (30),
nitrocellulose by Van Holde (48), and an epoxy resin by Ishai (55).

VII.   Strain Dependence of Stress Relaxation

There are few data on the variation of stress relaxation
with amplitude of deformation. However, the data do verify what
one would expect on the basis of the stress dependence of creep.
Although the stress relaxation modulus at a given time may be
independent of strain at small strains, at higher initial fixed

strains the stress or the stress relaxation modulus decreases
faster than expected, and the Boltzmann superposition principle
no longer holds.

Passaglia and Koppehele (74) found for cellulose monofilaments
that stress relaxation depended upon the initial strain——the
modulus decreased as strain increased. The shape of the stress
relaxation curves changes dramatically with the imposed elongation
for nylon and polyethylene terephthalate (75). Similar results
were found with polyethylenes (76-78). Polymers such as ABS
materials and polycarbonates which can undergo cold drawing
show especially rapid stress relaxation at elongations near the
yield point. As long as the initial elongations are low enough
for the stress-strain curve to be linear, the stress relaxes
slowly. However, in the region of the stress-strain curve where
the curve becomes nonlinear, the stress dies down much more
rapidly.

VIII. Effect of Pressure

Very few data are available on creep and stress relaxation
at pressures other than at one atmosphere. However, the data
are essentially what would be expected if pressure decreases
free volume and molecular or segmental mobility. DeVries and
Backman (79) found that a pressure of 50,000 psi decreases the
creep compliance of polyethylene by a factor of over ten.
Pressure increased the stress relaxation modulus a comparable
amount. At the higher pressures (30,000 psi), the stress
continued to relax for a much longer time than it did at one
atmosphere; pressure seems to shift some of the relaxation times
to longer times.

IX.   Thermal Treatments

Annealing of polymers decreases the rate of creep or stress relaxation at temperatures below the melting point or glass transition temperature.   Below T_g stress relaxes out faster in quenched specimens than in slowly cooled ones for amorphous polymers such as polymethyl methacrylate (80).   Quenched specimens of the same polymer have a creep rate at high loads which is as high as fifty times the rate for specimens annealed at 95°C for 24 hours (81).   The creep rate is strongly dependent upon the annealing temperature and the annealing time.   At temperatures just below T_g most of the effects due to annealing can be achieved in a short time.   However, greater effects are possible by annealing at lower temperatures, but the annealing times become very long.   Annealing affects the creep behavior at long times much more than it does the short times behavior (66). For instance, unplasticized polyvinyl chloride annealed at 60°C had nearly the same creep up to 1000 seconds for specimens annealed for one hour and for 2016 hours.   However, beyond 10,000 seconds, the specimen annealed for one hour had much greater creep than the specimen which had been annealed for 2016 hours (66) Findley (67) reports similar results on rigid polyvinyl chloride. Quenched amorphous polymers typically have densities from 10^{-4} to 10^{-2} g/cm^3 less than annealed polymers.   Thus, it appears that the free volume is an important factor in determining creep and stress relaxation in the glassy state, especially at long times.

Annealing can reduce the creep of crystalline polymers in the same manner as for glassy polymers (58,63,71).   However, for crystalline polymers such as polyethylene and polypropylene both

the annealing temperature and the test temperature are generally
between the melting point and T_g. Thus, for crystalline polymers
the cause of the decreased creep must be associated with the
degree of crystallinity, secondary crystallization, and changes
in the crystallite morphology brought about by the heat treatment.
Thus, the reduced rates in creep and stress relaxation brought
about by annealing and other heat treatments of crystalline
polymers are largely associated with changes in the crystalline
state while similar effects in amorphous polymers are largely
due to changes in free volume or density.

X. Effect of Molecular Weight; Rheology

At temperatures well below T_g where polymers are brittle,
their molecular weight has a minor effect on creep and stress
relaxation. This independence of properties on molecular weight
results from the very short segments of the molecules involved
in molecular motion in the glassy state. Motion of large
segments of the polymer chains is frozen-in, and the restricted
motion of small segments can take place without affecting the
remainder of the molecule. If the molecular weight is below
some critical value (82) or if the polymer contains a large
fraction of very low molecular weight material mixed in with
high molecular weight material, the polymer will be extremely
brittle and will have a lower than normal strength. Even these
weak materials will have essentially the same creep behavior as
the normal polymer as long as the loads or elongations are low.
At higher loads or elongations the weak low molecular weight
materials may break at considerably lower elongations than the
high molecular weight polymers.

Crazing occurs more easily in low molecular weight polymers; this can increase the creep or stress relaxation rate before failure takes place. The dependence of crazing on molecular weight of polystyrene in the presence of certain liquids is well illustrated by the data of Rudd (83). As a result of crazing by butanol, he found that the rate of stress relaxation is much faster for low molecular weight polystyrene than for high molecular weight material. This is to be expected since there are fewer than the normal number of chains carrying the load in crazed material. In addition, craze cracks act as stress concentrators which increase the load on some chains even more. These over-stressed chains tend to either break or slip so as to relieve the stress on them. Thus, in the glassy state, crazing is a major factor in stress relaxation and in creep (84,85). Crazing may also be at least part of the reason why creep in tension is generally greater than creep in compression since little, if any, crazing occurs in compression tests (86).

In the glass transition region the creep and stress relaxation become somewhat more dependent upon molecular weight, but it is only in the elastomeric region above T_g that the behavior becomes strongly dependent upon molecular weight. The important reason for this dependence on molecular weight for uncrosslinked, amorphous materials is because the mechanical response of such materials is determined by their viscosity and elasticity resulting from chain entanglements. When viscosity is the factor determining the creep behavior, the elongation versus time curve becomes a straight line, that is, the creep

rate becomes constant. The melt viscosity of polymers is
extremely dependent upon molecular weight as shown by Figure 14
(87). When the polymer chains are so short that they do not
become entangled with one another, the viscosity is approximately
proportional to the molecular weight. When the chains are so
long that they become strongly entangled, it becomes difficult
to move one chain past another. Thus, the viscosity becomes
very high, and it becomes proportional to the 3.4 or 3.5 power
of the molecular weight (88-91). The break in the curve of
Figure 14 gives the approximate molecular weight M_e at which
entanglements can occur. The entanglements not only increase
the viscosity but they act as temporary crosslinks and give rise
to rubber-like elasticity (92-95). (The value of M_e obtained
from viscosity measurements is approximately twice the value
calculated from the modulus equation of the kinetic theory of
rubber elasticity, which will be discussed later (1,9). This
result is what would be expected if half of a polymer chain
containing only one entanglement dangles on each side of the
point where the chain gets entangled with another chain.)

In general, the two sections of the curve in Figure 14 can
be represented by an equation of the form (87-92):

$$\log \eta = \log K_1 + K_2 \log M \tag{27}$$

The constant K_1 depends upon the structure of the polymer and
upon the temperature. The constant K_2 has different values
below and above M_e.

$$K_2 \doteq 1 \text{ for } M < M_e$$

$$K_2 = 3.4\text{-}3.5 \text{ for } M > M_e$$

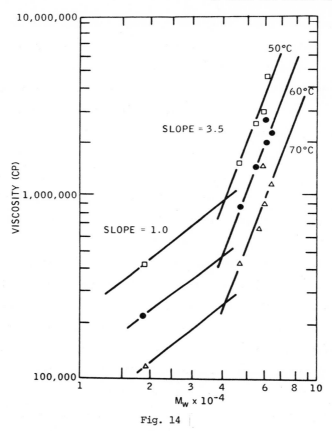

Fig. 14

Melt viscosity as a function of molecular weight for
butyl rubber. [Reprinted from Drexler, J. Appl. Polymer Sci.,
14, 1857 (1970).]

For sharp fractions, the value of all the molecular weight
averages are nearly the same. For unfractionated polymers and
polymer blends, M should be the weight average molecular weight
or better yet the viscosity average molecular weight.

The molecular theory of the viscosity of polymers predicts
an equation of the same form as equation 27. Bueche's (9,96)
theory as extended by Fox (92,97) gives:

$$\eta = \frac{N_O}{6}\left[\left(\frac{S_O^2}{M}\right)\frac{Z_e}{\bar{v}}\right]\left(\frac{Z_w}{Z_e}\right)^a \zeta \qquad (28)$$

where

$\quad a = 1$ for $Z_w < Z_e$

$\quad a \doteq 3.5$ for $Z_w > Z_e$.

In this equation N_O is Avogadro's number, $\bar{v}$ is the specific
volume, Z_w is the weight average number of atoms in the backbone
of the polymer chains, Z_e is the average number of atoms in the
backbone of the polymer chains between entanglements, ζ is the
friction factor per chain atom, and S_O^2 is the mean square
radius of gyration of the polymer chains. The chain length Z_w
may be calculated from the molecular weight M and the molecular
weight of the monomer M_O for monomers which have two backbone
atoms per monomer unit by

$$Z_w = 2M/M_O . \qquad (29)$$

The radius of gyration S_O^2 of polymers is generally determined
from light scattering measurements on dilute polymer solutions.
The friction factor, ζ, which is greatly increased by entanglements, is a measure of the force required to pull a polymer
chain through its surroundings at unit speed. It is inversely
proportional to the polymer self diffusion coefficient (9).
The friction factor ζ generally has a temperature dependence

given approximately by the Williams-Landel-Ferry Equation (15):

$$\log(\zeta/\zeta_g) \doteq \frac{-17.44(T - T_g)}{51.6 + T - T_g} \tag{30}$$

where ζ_g is the value of the friction coefficient at T_g.
Apparently for all polymers

$$\frac{S_o^2}{M}\left(\frac{Z_e}{\overline{V}}\right) \doteq 4.7 \times 10^{-15} . \tag{31}$$

Another theory emphasizing the importance of entanglements has
been developed by Chompff and Prins (98).

The molecular weight distribution, as well as the molecular
weight, affect the viscosity, creep compliance, and the stress
relaxation modulus (1,99-104). For blends made up of two
fractions of different molecular weight, the viscosity of the
blend η_ℓ is at a given temperature in some cases approximated by

$$\eta_\ell \doteq \phi_1 \ \lambda_1 \ \eta_1 + \phi_2 \ \lambda_2 \ \eta_2 \qquad , \tag{32}$$

where the subscripts refer to fractions 1 and 2, ϕ_1 is the
volume fraction of fraction 1, η_1 is the corresponding viscosity,
and λ is a factor which in some cases is given by (103):

$$\lambda_i \doteq \left(\frac{\overline{M}_{w\ell}}{\overline{M}_{wi}}\right)^{2.5} . \quad ; \quad i = 1,2. \tag{33}$$

$\overline{M}_{w\ell}$ is the weight average molecular weight of the blend, and
$\overline{M}_{wi}$ is the weight average molecular weight of component i. The
stress relaxation shear modulus of the blend, $G_\ell(t)$ is

$$G_\ell(t) \doteq \phi_1 \ G_1(t/\lambda_1) + \phi_2 \ G_2(t/\lambda_2) \tag{34}$$

while the steady state creep compliance J_e of the blend is

$$J_e \doteq \frac{\lambda_1^2 \, \eta_1^2 \, \phi_1 \, J_{e1} + \lambda_2^2 \, \eta_2^2 \, \phi_2 \, J_{e2}}{\eta_b^2} \, . \tag{35}$$

Note that in the case of the stress relaxation, the λ terms
are shift factors on the time scale used in making master
curves; the λ_i change the time scale from t to t/λ_i. The
theory for polymer blends is not very satisfactory, so the
above equations must be used with caution.

An example of experimental stress relaxation data is shown
in Figure 15 (104). Master stress relaxation curves made from
the experimental data on different molecular weight materials
are shown in Figure 16. The temperature shift factors used in

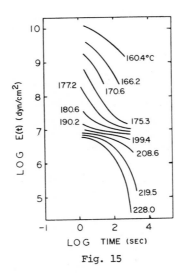

Fig. 15

Stress relaxation data on poly-α-methylstyrene at different
temperatures. Molecular weight is 460,000. [Reprinted
from Fujimoto, et al., J. Polymer Sci., A2, 6, 129 (1968).]

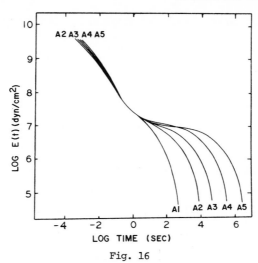

Fig. 16

Stress relaxation master curves for poly-α-methylstyrene of
different molecular weights. Reference temperature = 459°K.
[Reprinted from Fujimoto, et al., J. Polymer Sci., A2, 6,
129 (1968).]

------

making the master curves are shown in Figure 17. Note that the
shift factors a_T are the same for all molecular weights and
follow a W-L-F relation (13). The molecular weights covered the
range shown in the following table:

Sample Number	Molecular Weight
A1	39,000
A2	91,000
A3	135,000
A4	280,000
A5	460,000

The plateau in the stress relaxation modulus E(t) near 10^7 dynes/
cm^2 is due to the chain entanglements. The higher the molecular

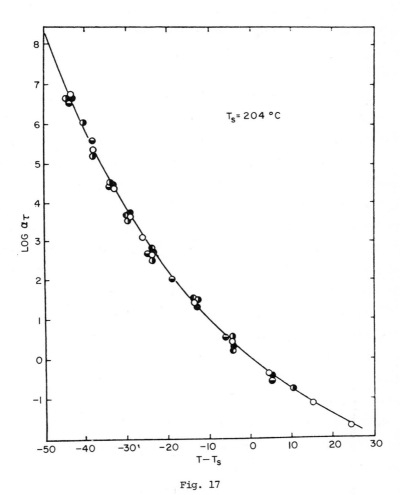

Fig. 17

W-L-F shift factors for different molecular weight poly-α-methylstyrenes. Reference temperature = 204°C.

[Reprinted from Fujimoto, et al., J. Polymer Sci., A2, 6, 129 (1968).]

weight, the longer it takes for the effects of the chain
entanglements to disappear. The polymers behave as viscous
liquids only at times beyond the plateau region where the
stress relaxation modulus decreases rapidly again. In the
plateau region the materials have elasticity and behave very
similar to vulcanized rubbers.

Chain branching affects the viscosity above T_g and,
therefore, influences creep and stress relaxation (105-109).
The effect is difficult to quantify because the length and
number of branches can vary, and the branches can all originate
at one point (as in a cross or star), or they can be spaced
along the chain (as in a comb). Molecules consisting of three
or four long branches of equal length, which are long enough to
form entanglements, have higher viscosity than linear polymers
of the same molecular weight at very slow rates of deformation.
At higher rates, however, the branched polymers have the
smaller melt viscosity (107). If a branched polymer is to have
a higher viscosity than a linear polymer of the same molecular
weight, the branches must be so long that they can have
entanglements (106). Otherwise, branched polymers have lower
viscosity than linear ones (110). Thus, branching can either
increase or decrease viscosity (109). Bueche (105) has
attempted to explain theoretically the effect of branching on
viscosity. The important factor is the ratio of the mean square
radius of the branched molecules to that of the linear polymer
of the same molecular weight, since branching changes the volume
occupied by a chain.

XI. Effect of Plasticizers on Melt Viscosity

Plasticizers or liquid diluents greatly reduce the melt

viscosity of polymers (92, 111-118). Small amounts of liquids at temperatures just above T_g produce an especially dramatic decrease in viscosity. Several factors are responsible for the decrease: 1. Liquids lower the glass transition temperature, and according to the W-L-F theory the viscosity and relaxation times are decreased. 2. Diluents increase the molecular weight between entanglements according to the equation

$$M_e = M_e^o / \phi_1 \tag{36}$$

where M_e^o is the molecular weight between entanglements for the undiluted polymer, and ϕ_1 is the volume fraction of polymer. 3. The mixing of a high viscosity liquid with one of low viscosity reduces the viscosity just because of the dilution of the polymer.

The theories of the viscosity of plasticized polymers are in a fairly primitive state. They are valid only in limited concentration ranges. Apparently no simple equation has been developed which is capable of expressing the viscosity over the entire concentration range. This fact is not surprising since in going from pure polymer at its T_g to the pure liquid, the viscosity may decrease by a factor of 10^{15}. At high concentrations of polymer, Bueche (9,113) proposes that the viscosity is proportional to the fourth power of the polymer concentration and a complex function of the free volume of the mixture. Kraus and Gruver (111) find that the 3.4 power fits experimental data better than the fourth power. They propose

$$\frac{\eta}{\eta_o} = \phi_1^{3.4} \left(\zeta / \zeta_o \right) \left(\overline{s^2} / \overline{s_o^2} \right) \tag{37}$$

where η_o is the viscosity of the undiluted polymer at a given
temperature, ϕ_1 is the volume fraction of polymer, ζ and ζ_o are
the segmental friction factors of the diluted and undiluted
polymer, and $\overline{S^2}$ and $\overline{S_o^2}$ are the mean squared radius of gyration
of the diluted and undiluted polymer. This last term indicates
that poor solvents should lower the viscosity more than a good
solvent. As the temperature increases, the factor $\left(\zeta\overline{S^2}\right)\Big/\left(\zeta_o\overline{S_o^2}\right)$
increases as a function of the ratio $\left(T-T_{gD}\right)\Big/\left(T-T_{gp}\right)$. The glass
transition temperatures of the polymer and diluent are T_{gp} and
T_{gD}, respectively.

XII. Crosslinking

Above the glass transition temperature T_g, the effect of
crosslinks is to decrease the importance of viscous flow and to
increase the elasticity of the material. Thus, crosslinking
gives creep curves which tend to level off to a constant
deformation at long times and stress relaxation curves which
level off to a finite instead of a zero stress at long times.
In an ideal rubber the stress remains constant at all times
during a stress relaxation test. The creep curve of an ideal
rubber shows a definite deformation on application of the load,
and the strain remains at this constant value until the load is
removed, at which time the rubber snaps back to its original
length. Thus, an ideal crosslinked rubber is a perfect spring.
However, in practice, crosslinked elastomers can have very
imperfect network structures which contain dangling chain ends,
loops in polymer chains, and branched molecules only partly
incorporated into the network, as well as molecules entrapped
in the network but not attached to it by chemical bonds (1, 119-

123). Thus, creep and stress relaxation data can vary a great
deal, depending upon the degree of crosslinking, the perfection
of the network, and the morphology of the network structure.
The chemical nature of the polymer chains is only of minor
importance.

Highly crosslinked rubbers swell less in good solvents than
lightly crosslinked ones (124, 125). For this reason, swelling
in solvents is often used to determine quantitatively the degree
of crosslinking. However, in many respects, mechanical tests
such as elastic moduli are more suitable for estimating the
degree of crosslinking. This topic will be discussed later
under the heading of the kinetic theory of rubber. The effect
of crosslinking (as indicated by swelling tests) on creep is
illustrated in Figure 18 (126). The degree of crosslinking is
given in terms of the swelling ratio q, which is defined as the
ratio of the volume of the swollen gel to the volume of the
unswollen gel.

A crude estimate of the perfection of the network structure
is given by the sol fraction, which is the fraction of the
crosslinked polymer that can be extracted by a good solvent.
The higher the sol fraction the less perfect is the network
structure. An especially important type of imperfection in
networks appears to be entrapped entanglements (122,123).
Unless both ends of each of the two chain segments involved in
an entanglement are attached to the network structure, the
entanglement can eventually disappear by dragging the unattached
branched segments through the network to relieve the applied
stress. These entrapped entanglements can have extremely long
relaxation or retardation times.

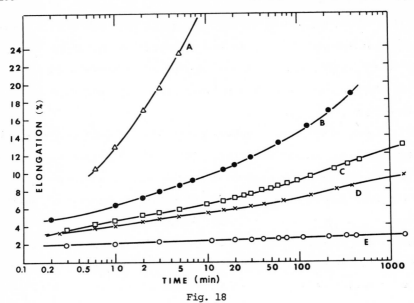

Fig. 18

Creep of SBR rubbers at 24°C.
- A. Uncrosslinked, $\overline{M}_w$ = 280,000.
- B. Lightly crosslinked, $M_c \doteq$ 29,000, q = 33.5, sol fraction = 34%.
- C. Moderately crosslinked, $M_c \doteq$ 18,200, q = 25.8, sol fraction = 24%.
- D. Moderately crosslinked, $M_c \doteq$ 14,400, q = 21, sol fraction = 20.4%.
- E. Highly crosslinked, $M_c \doteq$ 5200, q = 6.8, sol fraction = 9.5%. Swelling liquid was benzene. Load = 5 lb/in².
       [Reprinted from J. Appl. Polymer Sci., 8, 511 (1964).]

The uncrosslinked polymer in Figure 18 flows, so its deformation increases nearly linearly with time and its rate shows no tendency to decrease even at long times. Small degrees of crosslinking greatly decrease the creep rate, but creep still continues apparently forever (91, 127-131). Higher degrees of

crosslinking cut down both the creep and the creep rate, so that
after a time, the creep reaches essentially a limiting value
even though the creep rate may never drop completely to zero in
some cases. Farlie (132) has measured both the rate of creep
and the rate of stress relaxation of natural rubber as a function
of the degree of crosslinking. As expected from the results of
Figure 18, both rates decrease with crosslinking. Farlie's
results, and those of Berry and Watson (133), also illustrate
the effect of either network morphology or the chemical nature
of the crosslinking agent since the rates for sulfur
vulcanizates at a given degree of crosslinking are two or three
times as great as the rates found for peroxides as the
vulcanizing agent; the sulfide linkages in sulfur vulcanizates
may undergo interchange reactions which relieve the stress.
The great decrease in compliance that occurs when crosslinking
converts the polymer from a soluble material into a gel has
also been found for other rubbers such as polybutadiene (134)
and plasticized methacrylate (135).

Plazek (131) carried out very accurate creep experiments
on natural rubber as a function of crosslinking. He found that
data at different temperatures could be superimposed by the
usual W-L-F shift factors which were developed for non-crosslinked
polymers (15). Creep curves for different degrees of crosslinking
could be superimposed to give a master creep curve by horizontal
shifts and by vertical shifts determined by the degree of
crosslinking. The vertical shift factor is given by

$$\log\left(\frac{E(M_c)}{E\left(M_c^O\right)}\right)$$

where $E(M_c)$ is the long time equilibrium modulus of a rubber
with a molecular weight between crosslinks of M_c, while $E\left(M_c^O\right)$
is the equilibrium modulus of a reference rubber with a molecular
weight between crosslinks of M_c^O. The horizontal shifts are
determined primarily by the W-L-F relation, taking into account
that T_g may be raised by crosslinking, so that the horizontal
shift is also a function of the degree of crosslinking.

Although many creep measurements have been made on crosslinked polymers in the glassy state (thermosets such as phenol-
formaldehyde resins), these creep tests have mostly been of an
engineering nature and are of little scientific interest since
the degree of crosslinking was unknown. It appears that crosslinking has no major effect on the creep of polymers at
temperatures well below their glass transition region. In
rigid, brittle polymers, molecular motions are so frozen in
that the additional restrictions of crosslinks are hardly
noticeable. The creep of rigid polymers is strongly dependent
upon the elastic modulus, the mechanical damping, and the
difference between T_g and the ambient temperature. Some
thermoset materials such as phenol-formaldehyde and melamine
resins have high moduli, low mechanical damping, and high glass
transition temperatures; all of these factors tend to reduce
creep and creep rate, so these types of polymers generally
have low creep and very good dimensional stability. On the
other hand, some epoxy and polyester resins have much greater
creep. They may have shear moduli less than 10^{10} dynes/cm^2
because of low-temperature secondary glass transitions (136-139).
In addition, because of their chemical structure and low curing

temperature, many epoxy and polyester resins have relatively
low glass transition temperatures. For these reasons, such
resins may have considerably greater creep than the more highly
crosslinked phenolformaldehyde resins.

An effect of network morphology is illustrated by the work
of Shen and Tobolsky (121). They crosslinked rubbers in the
presence of inert diluents; such polymerizations tend to
promote intramolecular chain loops rather than interchain
crosslinks. Their polymers had very low stress relaxation
moduli compared to normal vulcanized rubbers containing similar
concentrations of crosslinking agent.

XIII. Crystallinity

Above T_g, crystallinity decreases creep compliance, creep
rate, and rate of stress relaxation while increasing the stress
relaxation modulus. Several theories have been developed to
explain these phenomena (140-146). These effects of crystallinity
come about from the apparent crosslinking as a result of many
chain segments being immobilized in the crystallites and from
the rigid crystallites acting as filler particles (140-142).
Figures 19 and 20 schematically illustrate the effects of
changing the degree of crystallinity on creep and stress
relaxation above T_g. (The shapes and absolute values of these
curves are rough approximations to any real polymer as the
properties can vary considerably from polymer to polymer. The
curves illustrate general trends as the degree of crystallinity
is changed.) Even small amounts of crystallinity can dramatically
decrease creep or stress relaxation without greatly increasing

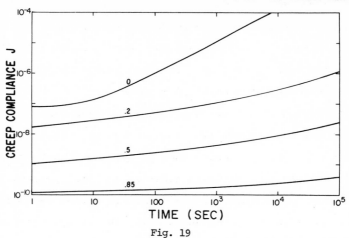

Fig. 19

Creep compliance as a function of degree of crystallinity above T_g. Numbers on curves are rough values of the degree of crystallinity.

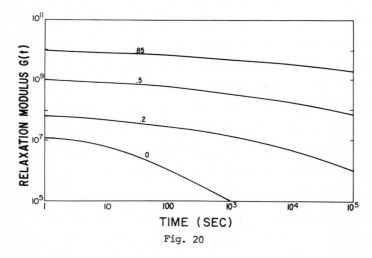

Fig. 20

Stress relaxation modulus as a function of crystallinity at temperatures above T_g. Numbers on the curves are rough values of the degree of crystallinity.

the modulus of the material (147-149). Plasticized polyvinyl
chloride film is an example; this elastomer maintains reasonable
dimensional stability for long periods of time without excessive
flow (147). The degree of crystallinity is so low, or the
crystallites are so imperfect that in many cases crystallinity
cannot be detected by x-ray diffraction. Polyvinyl alcohol
copolymers of low to moderate hydroxyl content are another
example (148). Polymers containing less than about 15 to 20
percent crystallinity behave essentially as crosslinked
rubbers(40,150,151). At crystallinities greater than about 40
or 50 percent, the crystallites may become a continuous phase
instead of just a dispersed phase in a rubbery matrix (146);
in such materials the modulus is high, and it becomes only very
slightly dependent upon time.

The temperature dependence of compliance and stress
relaxation modulus of crystalline polymers above T_g is greater
than that of crosslinked polymers, but in the glass transition
region the temperature dependence is less than for an amorphous
polymer. A factor in this large temperature dependence is the
decrease in the degree of crystallinity with temperature. Other
factors are the recrystallization of strained crystallites into
unstrained ones and the rotation of crystallites to relieve the
applied stress as well as the increased mobility in the
amorphous phase with temperature (25). All of these effects
occur more rapidly as the temperature is raised.

The distribution of relaxation or retardation times is much
broader for crystalline than for amorphous polymers. The
Boltzmann superposition principle often does not hold for
crystalline polymers at long times (58). Recrystallization and

other changes in the crystallites are the probable cause. The
W-L-F time-temperature superposition principle (15) generally
is not applicable to crystalline polymers except at low degrees
of crystallinity (40,58,148,149,152,153). This is again partly
due to the change of crystallinity and other factors with
temperature. In many cases master curves cannot be made for
crystalline polymers; in other cases master curves can be made
by using vertical as well as horizontal shifts of the experimental curves (23-25, 152, 153). The horizontal shifts may not
correspond to the usual W-L-F shifts, however. Figures 21 to 23
illustrate the typical differences in the stress relaxation
behavior of amorphous and crystalline materials (40). (It is
believed the values of crystallinity given on these curves are
low by a factor of at least two.) These figures show how
crystallinity flattens out the stress relaxation curves, i.e.,
broadens the distribution of relaxation times. In this case
of polycarbonate, the T_g appears to increase slightly with the
degree of crystallinity.

Annealing and also aging can change the degree of
crystallinity to some extent, but thermal treatments often
change the morphology more by increasing the length between
folds in the crystallites or by making spherulitic structure
more pronounced (154). Annealing and aging increase the
modulus and decrease the creep and stress relaxation rates (58,61)

Only a few representative cases of the hundreds of articles
on the creep and stress relaxation of crystalline polymers can
be referred to here. The creep of polyethylene has been
discussed by Carey (64), Findley (67), Turner (53), and
Nielsen (58). The stress relaxation of polyethylene has been

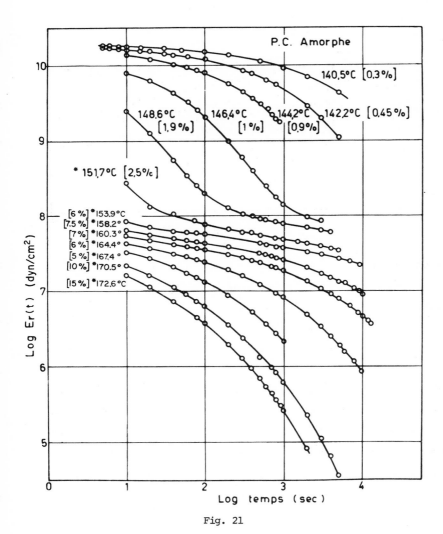

Fig. 21

Stress relaxation curves of amorphous bisphenol-A polycarbonate at the different temperatures shown by the curves.
The numbers in brackets are the maximum deformations used
in the tests. [Reprinted from Rheol. Acta 8, 510 (1969).]

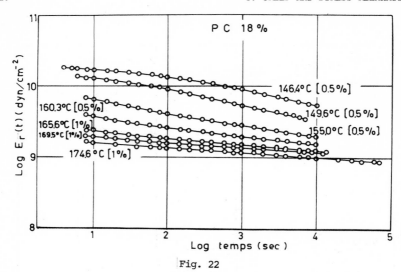

Fig. 22

Stress relaxation curves of crystalline bisphenol-A
polycarbonate at the temperatures shown by the curves. The
degreee of crystallinity was 18%. [Reprinted from Rheol.
Acta, 8, 510 (1969).]

studied by Becker (78), Catsiff (155), Nagamatsu (152), and
Faucher (20). Results on polypropylene are given by Faucher (20)
and Turner (61). The stress relaxation of polycarbonate over a
range of crystallinity is reported by Mercier (151), that of
nylon 6 by Yoshitomi (156) and Onogi (157), that of polyvinyl
acetals by Fujino (148), and that of fluorinated polymers by
Nagamatsu (158, 159). The creep of polyvinyl alcohol as
affected by water was studied by Yamamura and Kuramoto (160)
while the creep of a fluorinated polymer was investigated by
Findley and Khosla (161). The stress relaxation of polyoxymethylene was measured by Gohn and Fox (162).

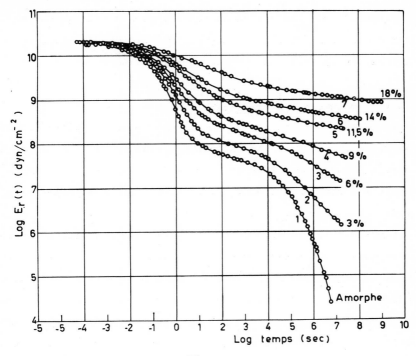

Fig. 23

Master stress relaxation curves of bisphenol-A polycarbonate
of different degrees of crystallinity. Degrees of
crystallinity are shown by curves. Reference temperature is
155°C. [Reprinted from Rheol. Acta, 8, 510 (1969).]

The stretching of amorphous but crystallizable materials
can greatly increase the rate of crystallization in some cases.
Natural rubber and polyethylene terephthalate are examples. The
stretching of the polymer causes the crystallites to grow so
that the chains in the crystallites are oriented parallel to
the applied stress. Thus, the growth of the crystallites

straightens out the coiled up chain segments and causes the
stress to relax rapidly or causes the specimen to elongate
rapidly in the case of a creep test (163,164).

XIV.   Copolymers and Plasticization

The primary effect of copolymerization and plasticizers
is to shift the glass transition temperature, so the creep and
stress relaxation curves are also shifted on the temperature
scale the same amount as T_g. Time-temperature superposition
still holds for such materials. However, two secondary effects
are often observed with both copolymers and plasticized polymers
that modify the creep and stress relaxation behavior somewhat.
Occasionally copolymerization and some plasticizers broaden the
glass transition region compared to the pure homopolymers (165-167)
This broadening can cause some decrease in $d\ell_T/dT$. A second
effect is sometimes found in the glassy state when plasticizers
are added to polymers with secondary glass transitions.   The
plasticizer (or comonomer) may increase the modulus in the
temperature region between the secondary and main glass transition
this effect has been called the antiplasticizer effect (168-170).

Water is a natural plasticizer for many polar polymers such
as the nylons (171), polyester resins (172), and cellulosic
polymers (173). Thus, the creep and stress relaxation behavior
of such polymers can be strongly dependent upon the relative
humidity of the atmosphere.

Polyvinyl chloride and its copolymers are probably the most
important polymers that are often used in the plasticized state.
Even though enough plasticizer is used to shift T_g well below room
temperature, the material does not show excessive flow or creep
even after long times under load. This behavior is very similar

to that of a crosslinked rubber. However, in this case there
are no chemical crosslinks; the material is held together by a
small amount of crystallinity——about 5 to 15 percent (147, 165).
The creep of plasticized polyvinyl chloride polymers as a function
of temperature, concentration, and kind of plasticizer has been
studied by many workers, including Aiken, Alfrey, Janssen, and
Mark (165), Nielsen, Buchdahl, and Levreault (167), and Sabia
and Eirich (174). These last workers also studied stress
relaxation (175).

In the case of crystalline polymers, plasticizers and
copolymerization reduce the melting point and the degree of
crystallinity. These factors tend to increase the creep and
stress relaxation, especially at temperatures approaching the
melting point.

XV. Effect of Orientation

Creep and stress relaxation are generally much less in the
direction parallel to the uniaxial orientation than they are
perpendicular to the orientation for rigid polymers (176-180).
At least part of this decreased creep must be due to the increased
modulus in the direction parallel to the oriented chains. For
instance, many highly oriented fibers have Young's moduli about
an order of magnitude greater than that of unoriented polymers.
Uniaxially oriented polyethylene made by cold-drawing has a
lower creep compliance (higher modulus) parallel to the
stretching direction than in the transverse direction (3). However, at 45° to the stretching direction, the modulus as
determined by a creep test is even less than the modulus of
unoriented polyethylene.

Analogous results have been found for stress relaxation.

In fibers, orientation increases the stress relaxation modulus
compared to the unoriented polymer (74,177,178,180). Orientation
also appears in some cases to decrease the rate, as well as the
absolute value, at which the stress relaxes, especially at long
times. However, in other cases, the stress relaxes more rapidly
in the direction parallel to the chain orientation in spite of
the increase in modulus (177,178,180). It appears that orientation can in some cases increase the ease with which one chain
can slip by another. This could result from elimination of some
chain entanglements or from more than normal free volume due to
the quench-cooling of oriented polymers.

Biaxially oriented films, made by stretching in two
mutually perpendicular directions, have reduced creep and stress
relaxation compared to unoriented materials. Part of the effect
is due to the increased modulus, but for brittle polymers, the
improved behavior can be due to reduced crazing. Biaxial
orientation generally makes crazing much more difficult in all
directions parallel to the plane of the film.

Another effect of orientation shows up as changes in
Poisson's ratio, which can be determined as a function of time
by combining the results of tension and torsion creep tests.
Poisson's ratio of rigid unoriented polymers remains nearly
constant or slowly increases with time. Orientation can
drastically change Poisson's ratio (181). Such anisotropic
materials actually have more than one Poisson's ratio. The
Poisson's ratio as determined when a load is applied parallel to
the orientation direction is expected to be greater than that of
the unoriented polymer, but this is not always the case,
especially for crystalline polymers such as polyethylene (179).

Although nearly all creep and stress relaxation tests are
made in uniaxial tension, it is possible to make biaxial tests
in which two stresses are applied at 90° to one another. In an
uniaxial test there is a contraction in the transverse direction,
but in a biaxial test the transverse contraction is prohibited.
As a result, biaxial creep is less than uniaxial creep——roughly
half as much. Biaxial strain ϵ_2 in each direction is (182,183):

$$\epsilon_2 = \frac{\sigma_o}{E} (1 - \nu) = \frac{\epsilon_1}{2} + \frac{\sigma_o}{6B} \qquad (38)$$

where ϵ_1 is the uniaxial strain that would result from a stress
σ_o, ϵ_2 is the biaxial strain in each of the mutually perpendicular
directions produced by the same stress σ_o in each direction,
ν is Poisson's ratio, and B is the bulk modulus. For most
polymers, Poisson's ratio is between 0.35 and 0.50, so biaxial
creep is generally between 50 and 65 percent as great as
uniaxial creep.

XVI.   Block Polymers and Polyblends

The mechanical properties of two-phase polymeric systems, such
as block and graft polymers and polyblends, will be discussed in
detail in Chapter 7. However, the creep and stress-relaxation
behavior of these materials will be examined at this point. Most
of the systems of practical interest consist of a combination of
a rubbery phase and a rigid phase. In many cases the rigid phase
is polystyrene since such materials are tough yet low in price.

Even in cases where the rigid polymer forms the continuous
phase, the elastic modulus is less than that of the pure matrix
material. Thus, two-phase systems have a greater creep

compliance than the pure rigid phase. Many of these materials
craze badly near their yield points. When crazing occurs, the
creep rate becomes much greater, and stress rapidly relaxes if
the deformation is held constant.

Several attempts have been made to superimpose creep and
stress relaxation data obtained at different temperatures on
styrene-butadiene-styrene block polymers. Shen and Kaelble (184)
found that William, Landel, Ferry (W-L-F)(15) shift factors held
around each of the glass transition temperatures of the polystyrene and the polybutadiene, but at intermediate temperatures
a different type of shift factor had to be used to make a master
curve. However, on very similar block polymers Lim, Cohen, and
Tschoegl (185) found that a W-L-F shift factor held only below
15°C in the region between the glass transitions, and at higher
temperatures an Arrhenius type of shift factor held. The reason
for this difference in the shift factors is not known. Master
curves have been made from creep and stress relaxation data on
partially miscible graft polymers of polyethyl acrylate and
polymethyl methacrylate (186). W-L-F shift factors held
approximately, but the master curves covered 20 to 25 decades of
time rather than the 10 to 15 decades for normal one-phase polymer

The properties of two-phase systems can be dramatically change
by casting the materials from different solvents. The effects are
due to changes in morphology and phase inversion which switches
one polymer from the continuous to the dispersed phase. Good
solvents for a polymer tend to make that polymer the continuous
phase, while poor solvents coil the polymer chains up tightly
and tend to force the polymer into being a dispersed phase.

Examples of the change in stress relaxation of styrene-rubber block polymers as a result of casting films from different kinds of solvents have been reported by Beecher, Marker, Bradford, and Aggarwal (187) and by Wilkes and Stein (188).

XVII. Summary

Creep and stress relaxation experiments cover long periods of time, so that they are sensitive to the types of molecular motions which require long times. These tests give little direct information on the types of molecular motion which take place at short times. However, by using time-temperature superposition principle and the W-L-F equations, access to these short times can be achieved even though they may not easily be attainable by direct experimentation.

Temperature is a major factor in determining creep and stress relaxation. This is partly because the absolute value of these mechanical properties depends upon the modulus of the polymer, and the modulus of a polymer can change by over a factor of 10^3 in a relatively short temperature range. In the neighborhood of the glass transition, the rate of change of properties with time as well as with temperature is great.

The mechanical properties of a polymer are determined by the distribution of relaxation or retardation times which in turn are determined by numerous structural and molecular factors as well as by environmental factors. At temperatures below T_g, the free volume is a major factor in determining the creep and stress relaxation behavior. Molecular motions cannot occur unless enough space is available, so that more types of

molecular motions can occur as the free volume increases. Free
volume can be reduced by lowering the temperature, annealing
at a temperature near T_g, or by increasing the pressure. All
of these factors tend to reduce the rate of creep or stress
relaxation. In glassy polymers below T_g the free volume may
be so low that very little creep or stress relaxation due to
molecular motion is possible. In such materials much of the
stress relaxation and creep is really due to crazing phenomena.

Molecular weight of the polymer is the most important
variable for amorphous polymers at temperatures above T_g
because the melt viscosity is strongly dependent upon molecular
weight. Above a critical value of molecular weight, materials
contain entanglements, which not only increase the viscosity
but also introduce rubber-like elasticity to the melts. These
entanglements impose restrictions on the motion of long chain
segments, so that additional long time relaxation and retardation
times are given to the polymer. Entanglements eventually
relax, but chemical crosslinks impose restrictions on chain
motions of a much more permanent nature. Thus, there is little,
if any, long term creep or stress relaxation for well crosslinked rubbers.

Crystallization ties polymer chains together and immobilizes
parts of the chains in the crystallites. The restrictions
resulting from crystallization are very similar to those due to
crosslinking as far as reducing creep and stress relaxation
are concerned at temperatures between T_g and the melting point.
The mechanical properties depend upon the degree of crystallinity
and the crystallite morphology; therefore, thermal history and

annealing can have unusually large effects on the behavior of
crystalline polymers.

Block polymers and similar two-phase systems are somewhat
analogous to crystalline materials at temperatures between the
lower T_g and the T_g or the melting point of the other phase.
The glassy (or crystalline phase) imposes restrictions on the
long range motions of the polymer chains with the lower T_g.
Thus, the creep or stress relaxation of two-phase systems is
quite small unless the temperature is above the softening
temperature of the higher softening component.

XVIII. Problems

1. A creep test is made on a polyethylene specimen which has
   a length of 4 inches, a width of 0.50 inches, and a thickness
   of 0.125 inches. A load of 62.5 pounds is applied to the
   specimen, and its length as a function of time is given by:

Time (minutes)	Length (Inches)
.1	4.033
1	4.049
10	4.076
100	4.110
1000	4.139
10,000	4.185

   Plot the creep compliance (cm^2/dyne) as a function of time
   using a logarithmic time scale. Would the curve show the
   upward curvature on a linear time scale?

2. Assuming that the Boltzmann superposition principle holds
   for the polymer in Problem 1, what would the creep elongation

be from 100 to 10,000 minutes if the load were doubled after 100 minutes?

3. Assuming that the Boltzmann superposition principle holds and that all of the creep is recoverable, what would the creep recovery curve be for the polymer in Problem 1 if the load were removed after 10,000 minutes?

4. Derive equation 6 for the elongation ε of a four-element model.

5. A material has two relaxation times——10 seconds and 100 seconds. Plot its relaxation curve from 1 second to 1000 seconds.

6. The creep of a polymer obeys the following equation:
$\varepsilon(t) = Kt^n \sinh (\sigma/\sigma_c)$ with n = 0.10, K = 10^{-5}, and σ_c = 1000 psi. Plot the creep curve for loads σ of 500, 1000, and 2000 psi from 1 second to 10^4 seconds. Why is it undesirable to apply loads greater than 1000 psi to this polymer for long periods of time?

7. A material has a viscosity of 10^4 poises at 0°C. If it obeys the W-L-F equation, what is its viscosity at 25°C? Assume the viscosity is 10^{13} poises at T_g.

8. A polymer degrades during processing from a weight average molecular weight of one million to 8 x 10^5. What is the ratio of the melt viscosity after processing to the melt viscosity before processing?

9. What will radiation during a test do to the stress relaxation of an elastomeric material if the radiation brings about chain scission? Compare a crosslinked polymer with a high molecular weight uncrosslinked one.

10. A horizontal cantilever beam is made of an idealized
    material which has only two retardation times——10 seconds
    and 1000 seconds. The beam is bent downward for 100 seconds.
    Then it is bent upwards for 1 second and released without
    any vibrations taking place. Describe the motion of the
    beam for the next 10,000 seconds.

11. A polymer above its T_g shows only a very slow creep rate.
    How would you distinguish between crosslinking and crystallin-
    ity as the cause of the small creep rate? Suggest at least
    two types of mechanical experiments or combinations of
    mechanical and other kinds of tests.

12. Use Figures 15 and 17 to construct the master curve for
    stress relaxation of the polymer at a reference temperature
    T_s of 204 °C.

13. In crosslinked rubbers in which there is a chemical reaction
    that involves breaking of network chains, the rate of
    reaction in many cases is given by

    $$dN/dt = -KN,$$

    where N is the number of network chains carrying stress
    at any time t. Show that the stress relaxation is

    $$\frac{\sigma(t)}{\sigma_o} = \exp(-Kt).$$

14. The distribution of relaxation times $H(\ln\tau)$ is a constant
    over several decades of time. What is the shape of the
    stress relaxation curve over this time interval?

15. Polymethyl methacrylate has a $T_g = 105°C$. How much faster
    is its rate of stress relaxation at 155°C than at 125°C?

XIX. References

1.   J. D. Ferry, Viscoelastic Properties of Polymers, 2nd Ed.,
      Wiley, New York, 1970.

2.   L. E. Nielsen, Mechanical Properties of Polymers, Van
      Nostrand Reinhold, New York, 1962.

3.   G. R. Smoluk, Modern Plast., 41, #12, 119 (1964).

4.   H. Leaderman, Rheology, Vol. 1, F. R. Eirich, Ed.,
      Academic Press, New York, 1958, p. 1.

5.   A. V. Tobolsky, Properties and Structure of Polymers, Wiley,
      New York, 1960.

6.   P. E. Rouse, Jr., J. Chem. Phys., 21, 1272 (1953).

7.   B. H. Zimm, J. Chem. Phys., 24, 269 (1956).

8.   F. Bueche, J. Chem. Phys., 22, 603, 1570 (1954).

9.   F. Bueche, Physical Properties of Polymers, Interscience
      New York, 1962.

10.   J. D. Ferry, R. F. Landel, and M. L. Williams, J. Appl. Phys.,
      26, 359 (1955).

11.   H. Leaderman, Elastic and Creep Properties of Filamentous
      Materials and Other High Polymers, Textile Foundation,
      Washington, D. C., 1943.

12.   P. Nutting, Proc. ASTM, 21, 1162 (1921).

13.   R. Buchdahl and L. E. Nielsen, J. Appl. Phys., 22, 1344
      (1951).

14.   E. Catsiff and A. V. Tobolsky, J. Colloid Sci., 10, 375
      (1955).

15.   M. L. Williams, R. F. Landel, and J. D. Ferry, J. Amer. Chem.

Soc., 77, 3701 (1955).

16. N. G. McCrum and E. L. Morris, Proc. Roy. Soc., A281, 258 (1964).

17. N. G. McCrum, B. E. Read, and G. Williams, Anelastic and Dielectric Effects in Polymeric Solids, Wiley, New York, 1967.

18. K. C. Rusch, J. Macromol. Sci., B2, 179 (1968).

19. N. Nemoto, M. Moriwaki, H. Odani, and M. Kurata, Macromol., 4, 215 (1971).

20. J. A. Faucher, Trans. Soc. Rheol., 3, 81 (1959).

21. K. Fujino, T. Horino, K. Miyamoto, and H. Kawai, J. Colloid Sci., 16, 411 (1961).

22. S. Onogi, T. Asada, Y. Fukui, and T. Fujisawa, J. Polymer Sci., A2, 5, 1067 (1967).

23. K. Nagamatsu, Kolloid Zeit., 172, 141 (1960).

24. R. W. Penn, J. Polymer Sci., A2, 4, 545 (1966).

25. Y. Fukui, T. Sato, M. Ushirokawa, T. Asada, and S. Onogi, J. Polymer Sci., A2, 8, 1195 (1970).

26. M. Takahashi, M. C. Shen, R. B. Taylor, and A. V. Tobolsky, J. Appl. Polymer Sci., 8, 1549 (1964).

27. N. Nemoto, Polymer J., 1, 485 (1970).

28. J. Bischoff, E. Catsiff, and A. V. Tobolsky, J. Amer. Chem. Soc., 74, 3378 (1952).

29. T. Murayama, J. H. Dumbleton, and M. C. Williams, J. Macromol. Sci., B1, 1 (1967).

30. E. Catsiff, T. Alfrey, Jr., and M. T. O'Shaughnessy, Textile Res. J., 23, 808 (1953).

31. J. R. McLoughlin and A. V. Tobolsky, J. Colloid Sci., 7,
     555 (1952).

32. K. Fujino, K. Senshu, and H. Kawai, J. Colloid Sci., 16,
     262 (1961).

33. E. Catsiff and A. V. Tobolsky, J. Appl. Phys., 25, 1092
     (1954).

34. A. V. Tobolsky and J. R. McLoughlin, J. Polymer Sci., 8,
     543 (1952).

35. R. L. Bergen, Jr. and W. E. Wolstenholme, SPE.J.,16, 1235
     (1960).

36. P. S. Theocoris, Kolloid Zeit., 236, 59 (1970).

37. K. Arisawa, H. Hirose, M. Ishikawa, T. Harada, and Y. Wada,
     Jap. J. Appl. Phys., 2, 695 (1963).

38. Y. Fukui, T. Sato, M. Ushirokawa, T. Asada, and S. Onogi,
     J. Polymer Sci., A2, 8, 1211 (1970).

39. D. J. Plazek, J. Colloid Sci., 15, 50 (1960).

40. J. P. Mercier and G. Groeninckx, Rheol. Acta, 8, 510 (1969).

41. J. Bares, J. Polymer Sci., A2, 9, 1271 (1971).

42. J. A. Sauer and W. J. Oliphant, Proc. ASTM, 49, 1119 (1949).

43. J. Marin and G. Cuff, Proc. ASTM, 49, 1158 (1949).

44. R. R. Dixon, SPE. J.., 14, #4, 23 (1958).

45. M. G. Sharma and P. R. Wen, Trans. SPE, 4, 282 (1964).

46. W. Kauzmann and H. Eyring, J. Amer. Chem. Soc., 62, 3113
     (1940).

47. A. V. Tobolsky and H. Eyring, J. Chem. Phys., 11, 125 (1943).

48. K. VanHolde, J. Polymer Sci., 24, 417 (1957).

49. D. R. Reid, British Plast., 32, 460 (1959).

50. D. R. Reid, Rheol. Acta, 1, 603 (1961).

51. W. N. Findley, SPE. J., 16, #1, 57 (1960).

52. D. O'Connor and W. N. Findley, Trans. SPE, 2, 273 (1962).

53. S. Turner, British Plast., 37, 501 and 567 (1964).

54. M. Goldstein, J. Polymer Sci., B4, 87 (1966).

55. O. Ishai, J. Appl. Polymer Sci., 11, 1863 (1967).

56. R. S. Moore and C. Gieniewski, Macromol., 1, 540 (1968).

57. L. E. Nielsen, J. Appl. Polymer Sci., 13, 1800 (1969).

58. L. E. Nielsen, Trans. Soc. Rheol., 13, 141 (1969).

59. F. Schwarzl, Kolloid Zeit., 165, 88 (1959).

60. F. H. Mueller and C. Engelter, Kolloid Zeit., 186, 36 (1962).

61. S. Turner, Trans. Plast. Inst., 31, 60 (1963).

62. R. L. Bergen, Jr., SPE. J., 23, #10, 57 (1967).

63. E. A. W. Hoff, P. L. Clegg, and K. Sherrard-Smith,
     British Plast., 31, 384 (1958).

64. R. H. Carey, Ind. Eng. Chem., 50, 1045 (1958).

65. G. R. Gohn and J. D. Cummings, ASTM Bull., No. 247, 64 (1960).

66. S. Turner, British Plast., 37, 682 (1964).

67. W. Findley, Trans. Plast. Inst., 30, 138 (1962).

68. H. Leaderman, Trans. Soc. Rheol., 7, 111 (1963).

69. J. A. Sauer, J. Marin, and C. C. Hsiao, J. Appl. Phys., 20,
     507 (1949).

70. R. S. Moore and C. Gieniewski, Polymer Eng. Sci., 9, 190
     (1960).

71. S. Turner, British Plast., 37, 440 (1964).

72. I. M. Ward and J. M. Wolfe, J. Mech. Phys. Solids, 14, 131 (1966).

73. M. G. Sharma and L. Gesinski, Modern Plast., 40, No. 5, 164 (1963).

74. E. Passaglia and H. P. Koppehele, J. Polymer Sci., 33, 281 (1958).

75. R. Meredith and B. Hsu, J. Polymer Sci., 61, 253 (1962).

76. O. Nakada, T. Hirai, and Y. Maeda, J. Japan. Soc. Testing Mater., 8, 284 (1959).

77. G. W. Becker and H. J. Rademacher, J. Polymer Sci., 58, 621 (1962).

78. G. W. Becker, Kolloid Zeit., 175, 99 (1961).

79. K. L. DeVries and D. K. Backman, J. Polymer Sci., B9, 717 (1971).

80. J. R. McLoughlin and A. V. Tobolsky, J. Polymer Sci., 7, 658 (1951).

81. D. H. Enders, J. Macromol. Sci., B4, 635 (1970).

82. E. H. Merz, L. E. Nielsen, and R. Buchdahl, Ind. Eng. Chem., 43, 1396 (1951).

83. R. F. Rudd, J. Polymer Sci., B1, 1 (1963).

84. L. Z. Rogovina and G. L. Slonimskii, Polymer Sci. (USSR), 8, 236 (1966).

85. G. Menges and H. Schmidt, Kunststoffe, 57, 885 (1967).

86. D. A. Thomas, Plastics and Polymers, 37, 485 (1969).

87. L. H. Drexler, J. Appl. Polymer Sci., 14, 1857 (1970).

88. T. G. Fox and P. J. Flory, J. Phys. Chem., 55, 221 (1951).

89. T. G. Fox and S. Loshaek, J. Appl. Phys., 26, 1080 (1955).

90. F. Bueche, J. Chem. Phys., 25, 599 (1956).

91. F. Bueche, J. Polymer Sci., 25, 305 (1957).

92. G. C. Berry and T. G. Fox, Adv. In Polymer Sci., 5, 261
     (1968).

93. L. E. Nielsen and R. Buchdahl, J. Chem. Phys. 17, 839 (1949).

94. L. E. Nielsen and R. Buchdahl, J. Colloid Sci., 5, 282 (1950).

95. H. Markovitz, T. G. Fox, and J. D. Ferry, J. Phys. Chem., 66,
     1567 (1962).

96. F. Bueche, J. Chem. Phys., 20, 1959 (1952).

97. T. G. Fox and V. R. Allen, J. Chem. Phys., 41, 337 and 344
     (1964).

98. A. J. Chompff and W. Prins, J. Chem. Phys., 48, 235 (1968).

99. R. L. Ballman and R. H. M. Simon, J. Polymer Sci., A2, 3557
     (1964).

100. R. Longworth and W. F. Busse, Trans. Soc. Rheol., 6, 179
     (1962).

101. K. Ninomiya, J. Colloid Sci., 14, 49 (1959).

102. K. Ninomiya, J. Colloid Sci., 17, 759 (1962).

103. K. Ninomiya and J. D. Ferry, J. Colloid Sci., 18, 421 (1963).

104. T. Fujimoto, M. Ozaki, and M. Nagasawa, J. Polymer Sci.,
     A2, 6, 129 (1968).

105. F. Bueche, J. Chem. Phys., 40, 484 (1964).

106. V. C. Long, G. C. Berry, and L. M. Hobbs, Polymer, 5,
     517 (1964).

107. G. Kraus and J. T. Gruver, J. Polymer Sci., A3, 105 (1965).

108. J. E. Guillet, R. L. Combs, D. F. Slonaker, D. A. Weems,
      and H. W. Coover, Jr., J. Appl. Polymer Sci., 9, 757 and
      767 (1965).

109. R. P. Chartoff and B. Maxwell, J. Polymer Sci., A2, 8, 455
      (1970).

110. J. S. Ham, J. Chem. Phys., 26, 625 (1957).

111. G. Kraus and J. T. Gruver, Trans. Soc. Rheol., 9, #2,
      17 (1965).

112. L. J. Garfield and S. E. Petrie, J. Phys. Chem., 68, 1750
      (1964).

113. F. N. Kelley and F. Bueche, J. Polymer Sci., 50, 549 (1961).

114. R. N. Haward, Chem. and Ind., #33, 1442 (Aug. 1964).

115. H. Fujita and E. Maekawa, J. Phys. Chem., 66, 1053 (1962).

116. G. Pezzin, J. Appl. Polymer Sci., 10, 21 (1966).

117. L. Utracki and R. Simha, J. Polymer Sci., Al, 1089 (1963).

118. P. F. Lyons and A. V. Tobolsky, Polymer Eng. Sci., 10, 1
      (1970).

119. L. E. Nielsen, J. Macromol. Chem., C3, 69 (1969).

120. A. R. H. Tawn, J. Oil Colour Chem. Assoc., 52, 814 (1969).

121. M. C. Shen and A. V. Tobolsky, J. Polymer Sci., A2, 2513
      (1964).

122. N. R. Langley, Macromol., 1, 348 (1968).

123. N. R. Langley and J. D. Ferry, Macromol., 1, 353 (1968).

124. P. J. Flory, Chem. Rev., 39, 137 (1946).

125. P. J. Flory, Principles of Polymer Chemistry, Cornell University, Ithaca, 1953.

126. L. E. Nielsen, J. Appl. Polymer Sci., 8, 511 (1964).

127. F. Bueche, J. Appl. Polymer Sci., 1, 240 (1959).

128. L. A. Wood, Nat. Bur. Stds. (U.S.), Report 5796 (May 12, 1958).

129. L. A. Wood, J. Rubber Res. Inst. Malaya, 22, 309 (1969); Rubber Chem. Tech., 43, 1482 (1970).

130. L. A. Wood and G. W. Bullman, J. Polymer Sci., A2, 10, 43 (1972).

131. D. J. Plazek, J. Polymer Sci., A2, 4, 745 (1966).

132. E. D. Farlie, J. Appl. Polymer Sci., 14, 1127 (1970).

133. J. P. Berry and W. F. Watson, J. Polymer Sci., 18, 201 (1955).

134. R. H. Valentine, J. D. Ferry, T. Homma, and K. Ninomiya, J. Polymer Sci., A2, 6, 479 (1968).

135. J. Janácék and J. D. Ferry, Rheol. Acta, 9, 208 (1970).

136. A. S. Kenyon and L. E. Nielsen, J. Macromol. Sci., A3, 275 (1969).

137. C. A. May and F. E. Weir, SPE. Trans., 2, 207 (1962).

138. F. R. Dammont and T. K. Kwei, J. Polymer Sci., A2, 761 (1967).

139. K. Shibayama and Y. Suzerki, J. Polymer Sci., A3, 2637 (1965).

140. A. V. Tobolsky, J. Chem. Phys., 37, 1139 (1962).

141. A. V. Tobolsky and V. D. Gupta, Textile Res. J., 33, 761 (1963).

142. L. E. Nielsen and F. D. Stockton, J. Polymer Sci., A1, 1995 (1963).

143. F. Bueche, J. Polymer Sci., 22, 113 (1956).

144. P. J. Flory, Trans. Faraday Soc., 51, 848 (1955).

145. W. R. Krigbaum, R. J. Roe, and K. J. Smith, Jr., Polymer, 5 533 (1964).

146. A. Bondi, J. Polymer Sci., A2, 5, 83 (1967).

147. T. Alfrey,Jr., N. Wiederhorn, R. S. Stein, and A. V. Tobolsky, J. Colloid Sci., 4, 211 (1949).

148. K. Fujino, K. Senshu, T. Horino, and H. Kwai, J. Colloid Sci., 17, 726 (1962).

149. A. Crugnola, M. Pegoraro, and F. Danusso, J. Polymer Sci., A2, 6, 1705 (1968).

150. L. E. Nielsen, J. Appl. Polymer Sci., 2, 351 (1959).

151. J. P. Mercier and G. Groeninckx, Rheol. Acta, 8, 504 (1969).

152. K. Nagamatsu, T. Takemura, T. Yoshitomi, and T. Takemoto, J. Polymer Sci., 33, 515 (1958).

153. T. Takemura, J. Polymer Sci., 38, 471 (1959).

154. P. H. Geil, Polymer Single Crystals, Interscience, New York, 1963.

155. E. Catsiff, J. O. Offenbach, and A. V. Tobolsky, J. Colloid Sci., 11, 48 (1956).

156. T. Yoshitomi, K. Nagamatsu, and K. Kosiyama, J. Polymer Sci., 27, 335 (1958).

157. S. Onogi, K. Sasaguri, T. Adachi, and S. Ogihara, J. Polymer Sci., 58, 1 (1962).

158. K. Nagamatsu, T. Yoshitomi, and T. Takemoto, _J. Colloid Sci._, 13, 257 (1958).

159. K. Nagamatsu and T. Yoshitomi, _J. Colloid Sci._, 14, 377 (1959).

160. H. Yamamura and N. Kuramoto, _J. Appl. Polymer Sci._, 2, 71 (1959).

161. W. N. Findley and G. Khosla, _SPE. J._, 12, #12, 20 (1956).

162. G. R. Gohn and A. Fox, _Materials Res. Stds._, 1, 957 (1961).

163. A. Gent, _Trans. Faraday Soc._, 50, 521 (1954).

164. A. V. Tobolsky, and G. M. Brown, _J. Polymer Sci._, 17, 547 (1955).

165. W. Aiken, T. Alfrey, Jr., and H. Mark, _J. Polymer Sci._, 2, 178 (1947).

166. L. E. Nielsen, _J. Am. Chem. Soc._, 75, 1435 (1953).

167. L. E. Nielsen, R. Buchdahl, and R. Levreault, _J. Appl. Phys._, 21, 607 (1950).

168. W. J. Jackson,Jr. and J. R. Caldwell, _Adv. Chem. Series_, 48, 185 (1965).

169. W. J. Jackson,Jr. and J. R. Caldwell, _J. Appl. Polymer Sci._, 11, 211, 227 (1967).

170. L. M. Robeson and J. A. Faucher, _J. Polymer Sci._, B7, 35 (1969).

171. S. Turner, _British Plast._, 38, 44 (1965).

172. N. A. Brunt, _Kolloid Zeit._, 185, 119 (1962).

173. M. T. O'Shaughnessy, _Textile Res. J._, 18, 263 (1948).

174. R. Sabia and F. R. Eirich, _J. Polymer Sci._, A1, 2511 (1963).

175. R. Sabia and F. R. Eirich, _J. Polymer Sci._, A1, 2497 (1963).

176. G. B. Jackson and J. L. McMillan, _SPE. J._, 19, 203 (1963).

177. R. G. Cheatham and A. G. H. Dietz, _Trans. ASME_, 74, 31 (1952).

178. R. G. Cheatham and A. G. H. Dietz, _Modern Plastics_, 29, 113 (Sept. 1951).

179. M. W. Darlington and D. W. Saunders, _J. Macromol. Sci._, B5, 207 (1971).

180. C. D. Pomeroy, _British J. Appl. Phys._, 12, 3 (1961).

181. M. J. Bonnin, C. M. R. Dunn, and S. Turner, _Plastic Polymers_, 37, 517 (1969).

182. S. Timoshenko and J. N. Goodier, _Theory of Elasticity_, 2nd Ed., McGraw-Hill, New York, 1951, p. 7.

183. F. L. McCrackin and C. F. Bersch, _SPE. J._, 15, 791 (1959).

184. M. Shen and D. H. Kaelble, _J. Polymer Sci._, B8, 149 (1970).

185. C. K. Lim, R. E. Cohen, and N. W. Tschoegl, _Adv. Chem. Series_, 99, 397 (1971).

186. L. H. Sperling, H. F. George, V. Huelck, and D. A. Thomas, _J. Appl. Polymer Sci._, 14, 2815 (1970).

187. J. F. Beecher, L. Marker, R. D. Bradford, and S. L. Aggarwal, _J. Polymer Sci._, C26, 117 (1969).

188. G. L. Wilkes and R. S. Stein, _J. Polymer Sci._, A2, 7, 1525 (1969).

Chapter 4

Dynamic Mechanical Properties

I. Introduction and Instruments

The general nature of dynamic mechanical tests, the
definitions, and the kinds of instruments used in making such
tests were discussed in Chapter 1. The equations for calculating
damping also were given in Chapter 1, and the equations for
calculating the moduli from various vibration tests were given
in Chapter 2. Dozens of dynamic mechanical instruments have
been described in the literature. General references discussing
many kinds of instruments are Ferry (1,2) and Nielsen (3). A
summary of part of the literature on various instruments is
given in Table 1 (1-63). Some instruments are for rubbers
and polymer melts whereas others are for rigid polymers or
fibers; some instruments cover a wide range of temperatures
while others cover a wide frequency range. No single instrument
can cover the complete range of materials, temperature, and
frequency.

The dynamic mechanical behavior of polymers is of great
interest and importance for many reasons. The dynamic modulus,
or the modulus measured by any other technique, is one of the
most basic of all mechanical properties, and its importance in
any structural application is well known. The role of
mechanical damping, however, is not so well known. Damping

Table 1

Dynamic Mechanical Testing Instruments

Reference No.	Type of Instrument
1	General reference on many types of instruments.
2	General reference on many types of instruments.
3	General reference on many types of instruments.
4	General reference on several types of instruments.
5	Several types of instruments.
6	Several types of instruments.
7	Torsion pendulum
8	Torsion pendulum
9	Torsion pendulum
10	Torsion pendulum
11	Torsion pendulum
12	Torsion pendulum
13	Torsion pendulum
14	Torsion pendulum (Gels and rubbers)
15	Torsion pendulum (Cryogenic temperatures)
16	Torsion pendulum (Both G' and E')
17	Torsion pendulum
18	Torsion pendulum (Both G' and E')
19	Torsion pendulum (Stiff wire suspension)
20	Torsion pendulum (Cone and plate for gels)
21	Torsion pendulum
22	Torsion pendulum (Direct reading)
23	Torsion pendulum (Stiff wire suspension)
24	Torsion pendulum
25	Torsion pendulum and 2 other instruments
26	Torsion pendulum
27	Torsion pendulum (Torsional braid analysis)
28	Torsion pendulum (Torsional braid analysis)
29	Torsion pendulum (Cryogenic temperatures)
30	Torsion pendulum (Torsional braid analysis)
31	Vibrating reed
32	Vibrating reed
33	Vibrating reed
34	Vibrating reed and two other instruments

Table 1 (Continued)

Reference No.	Type of Instrument
35	Vibrating reed (optical recording)
36	Vibrating reed
37	Vibrating reed (Mass on end)
38	Vibrating reed
39	Vibrating reed (Low loss materials at low temperature)
40	Vibrating reed (Multiple samples)
41	Vibrating reed (Cryogenic temperatures)
42	Free resonating beam
43	Rotating beam
44	Rotating beam
45	Rotating beam (Modified for shear)
46	Nonresonance forced vibrations (rubbers)
47	Nonresonance forced vibrations (rubbers)
48	Nonresonance forced vibrations
49	Nonresonance forced vibrations (Fitzgerald apparatus)
50	Nonresonance forced vibrations (Electromagnetic drive)
51	Nonresonance forced vibrations (Commercial apparatus)
52	Nonresonance forced vibrations (Liquids and gels)
53	Nonresonance forced vibrations (Rubbers)
54	Nonresonance forced vibrations (Rubbers, several instruments)
55	Nonresonance forced vibrations
56	Nonresonance forced vibrations (Large frequency range)
57	Nonresonance forced vibrations (Several instruments)
58	Nonresonance forced vibrations
59	Nonresonance forced vibrations (Wide modulus range)
60	Nonresonance forced vibrations (Commercial instrument)
61	Ultrasonic instrument (Six instruments)
62	Ultrasonic instrument (Both E^* and G^*)
63	Ultrasonic instrument (For fibers)

is often the most sensitive indicator of all kinds of molecular
motions which are going on in a material, even in the solid
state. Aside from the scientific interest in understanding
the molecular motions which can occur, these motions are of
great practical importance in determining the mechanical
behavior of polymers. For this reason, the absolute value of
the damping and the temperature and frequency at which damping
peaks occur are of considerable interest.

High damping is sometimes an advantage and sometimes a
disadvantage. For instance, high damping in a car tire tends
to give better friction to the road surface, but at the same
time, damping causes heat build-up which causes a tire to degrade
more rapidly. Damping reduces vibrations (mechanical and
acoustical) and prevents resonance vibrations from building up
to dangerous amplitudes. However, high damping is generally an
indication of reduced dimensional stability which can be very
undesirable in structures carrying loads for long periods of
time. Many other mechanical properties are intimately related
to damping; these include fatigue life, toughness and impact
strength, wear, and coefficient of friction.

The dynamic mechanical properties, especially the damping,
are extremely sensitive to all kinds of transitions, relaxation
processes, structural heterogeneities, and the morphology of
multiphase systems such as crystalline polymers, polyblends,
and filled or composite materials. The damping also may be
used as a powerful analytical tool for measuring molecular
weights, composition of copolymers, the degree and heterogeneity
of crosslinking, the effect of heat treatments on the crystallite
morphology of crystalline polymers, the composition of polyblends

and block polymers, and the extent of curing reactions in
thermoset resins.

II. Temperature and Frequency Effects

The effect of temperature on the modulus of a typical
polymer already has been presented in Chapter 2. It will be
recalled that there is a great decrease in the modulus in the
temperature range of the glass transition. Molecular weight,
crosslinking, crystallinity, and plasticization each give rise
to distinctive characteristics in the modulus-temperature
curve. The dynamic modulus-temperature curves are essentially
the same as those shown in Chapter 2. In a dynamic test the
frequency (or time scale of the test) should be held approximately
constant as the temperature is changed. Figure 1 illustrates
the effect of frequency on the modulus and damping curves.
The amount of shift on changing the frequency depends upon the
absolute temperature of T_g and on its energy of activation, ΔH.
For a factor of 10 increase in frequency the inflection point
in the modulus curve or the maximum in the damping peak will be
shifted from T_1 to T_2 °K according to the equation (3)

$$\left(\frac{1}{T_1} - \frac{1}{T_2}\right) = \frac{2.303R}{\Delta H} \tag{1}$$

where R is the gas constant. Table 2 gives the shift in
temperature for various values of T_1 and ΔH. For the main glass
transition where $T_1 = T_g$, the energy of activation is of the
order of 10^5 calories per mole. For secondary transitions at
cryogenic temperatures, ΔH is of the order of 10^3 to 10^4
calories/mole. For most polymers, T_g and the maximum in the

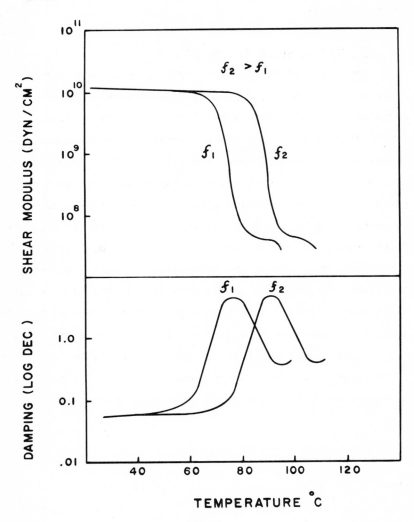

Fig. 1

The modulus and damping of a typical amorphous polymer as a
function of temperature at two frequencies. Frequency
f_2 is greater than f_1.

Table 2

Temperature Shifts for a Decade Change in Frequency

Temperature ($°K$)	Activation Energy ΔH (cal./mole)	Temperature Shift for a Factor of Ten Increase in Frequency; $(T_2 - T_1)$ ($°K$)
50	1×10^4	1.2
100	1×10^4	4.8
200	1×10^4	20.2
200	5×10^4	3.7
200	1×10^5	1.8
300	1×10^4	48.5
300	5×10^4	8.5
300	1×10^5	4.2
400	1×10^4	89.6
400	5×10^4	15.2
400	1×10^5	7.5

damping peak are increased about 7°C for a factor of ten increase in frequency.

Figures 1 and 2 (64) illustrate the simplest dynamic mechanical properties curves of common polymers as a function of temperature.

At the point where the modulus-temperature curve has an inflection point, the damping curve goes through a large maximum. The damping in these curves is expressed as the ratio of the loss modulus or the imaginary modulus M" to the real part of the modulus M' or its equivalent, tan δ. (M can refer to either the shear modulus G or Young's modulus E.)

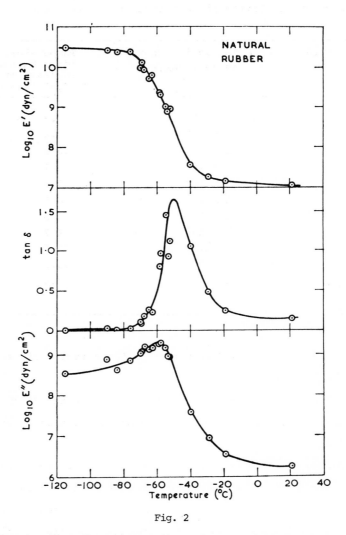

Fig. 2

The dynamic mechanical properties of natural rubber as a
function of temperature. [Reprinted from Read, Proc. 5th
Internat. Congr. Rheol., 4,71 (1970).]

The imaginary modulus (a term proportional to the energy dissipated as heat) goes through a less prominent peak than tan δ, and the maximum in the M" curve occurs at a slightly lower temperature than the peak in the M"/M' or tan δ curve.

Damping measures the imperfection in the elasticity, that is, damping reduces the "snap" of a material. In high damping materials and especially in the damping peak, much of the energy used to deform a material is dissipated directly into heat. At the temperature of maximum damping, polymers have a "dead" or leathery feel. A material with Newtonian viscosity is the extreme case of infinite damping in which all the energy used to deform the material is dissipated into heat. A perfectly elastic substance such as an ideal spring exhibits no damping.

The damping peak is associated with the partial loosening of the polymer structure so that groups and small chain segments can move. This occurs near T_g at low frequencies. The tan δ peak at a frequency of one cycle per second generally is at a temperature 5°C to 15°C above the glass transition temperature as measured by dilatometry or differential thermal analysis (DTA). The maximum in the loss modulus M" at low frequencies is very close to T_g. At temperatures well below T_g the damping can be small; nearly all the energy stored in deforming the material is quickly recovered when the stress is removed since molecular slipping and other motions are frozen in. However, in the glass transition region, some molecular chain segments are frozen-in while some are free to move. If the stress is initially applied to a frozen-in chain segment which later becomes free to move while it is still under stress, the

segment will move in such a manner as to reduce the stress on
it. After moving, the segment has less stored energy because
of the reduction in stress, so the excess energy was dissipated
as heat. This delayed response causes the deformation to lag
behind the applied stress by a phase angle δ which is related
to the damping by

$$\tan \delta = M''/M'. \qquad\qquad (2)$$

The four-element model used to illustrate creep behavior
in Chapter 3 also can be used to show how damping changes with
temperature. The dynamic mechanical properties of this model
are shown in Figure 3 (65). Assume that the viscosity of the
dashpots decreases with temperature, and the viscosity of the
single dasphot η_3 is greater than that of the middle one η_2.
At very low temperatures the viscosity will be so high that
the dashpots are frozen and will not respond to a force, so
only the single spring E_1 stretches, and the damping will be
very low. At a higher temperature the viscosity will have
decreased enough for the middle dashpot η_2 in parallel with
the second spring E_2 to respond to a stress. Now, a stress
initially stretches the single spring, but the middle spring
and dashpot also will stretch as the stress continues. The
middle section lags behind the applied stress, and when the
periodic external stress again becomes zero, the middle
section will still be partly stretched and will continue to
decrease in length. Thus, the stress and strain are not in
phase. The motion of the viscous dashpot η_2 dissipates energy
into heat, and in this temperature interval the damping will

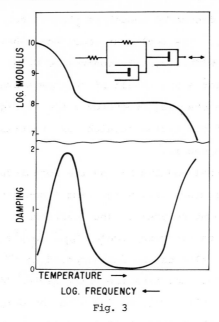

Fig. 3

Dynamic mechanical properties of a 4-element model as a function
of temperature or as a function of the logarithm of the
frequency.

---

be high. At somewhat higher temperatures the viscosity of the
single dashpot η_3 is still too great for it to respond much
to a stress, but the viscosity of the middle dashpot will be
very low. Now both springs readily respond to a stress, so
the modulus will be lower. The damping will also be fairly
small since the viscosity of the dashpot is too low to dissipate
much energy in spite of its large motion. (The energy dissipated
is proportional to the product of the viscosity and the velocity.)
At still higher temperatures well above the damping peak, the
damping can again increase when the viscosity of the single

dashpot η_3 has decreased enough so that it can respond to the
external stress.   The 4-element model now behaves similar to a
molten polymer with viscosity controlled by molecular slippage.
Curves of similar shape result if the temperature scale is replaced by an inverse log frequency scale in Figure 3; that is,
the response of the system to high temperatures is similar to
that at low frequencies.

Both the real modulus M' and the loss modulus M" curves as a
function of frequency follow the time-temperature superposition
principle for many polymers.   The logarithmic time scale is
replaced by a log frequency scale.   The complex compliances,
both J' and J", also can be superimposed to give master curves.
For most amorphous polymers the shift factors are given by the
W-L-F equation (66).   Figures 4-7 give the original dynamic
data on polyvinyl acetate obtained at various frequencies and
temperatures along with the constructed master curves for J'
and J" as a function of the reduced frequency ωa_T (67).   (The
time-temperature shift factor a_T is the same as that discussed
in Chapter 3.)   The master curves may be used to calculate a
distribution of relaxation or retardation times, which in turn
can be used to calculate other mechanical properties such as
stress relaxation.   Figure 8 shows the distributions of
relaxation and retardation times as calculated from the master
curves given in Figures 6 and 7.   The data also can be given
as master curves for the shear moduli G' and G" and for the
viscosity η' as shown in Figure 9.   The elasticity increases
with reduced frequency ωa_T, but the viscosity decreases with
frequency.   Polymer melts are very non-Newtonian in behavior

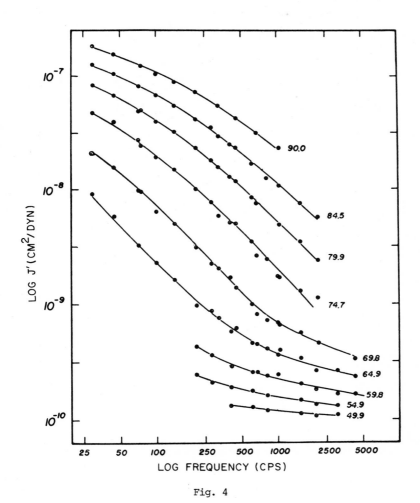

Fig. 4

Dynamic shear compliance J' as a function of frequency for
polyvinyl acetate at the temperatures indicated.   [Reprinted
from Williams and Ferry, <u>J. Colloid Sci.</u>, 9, 479 (1954).]

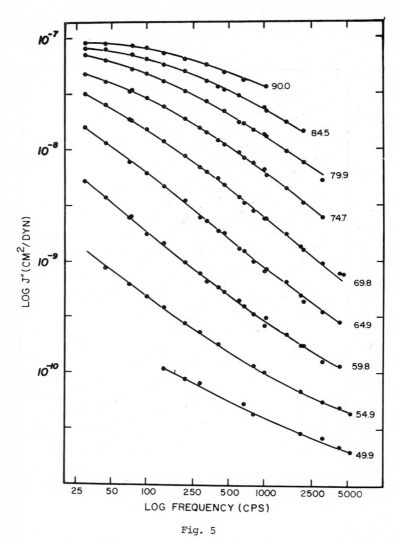

Fig. 5

Variation of the loss compliance J" with frequency for
polyvinyl acetate at the temperatures indicated. [Reprinted
from Williams and Ferry, J. Colloid Sci., 9, 479 (1954).]

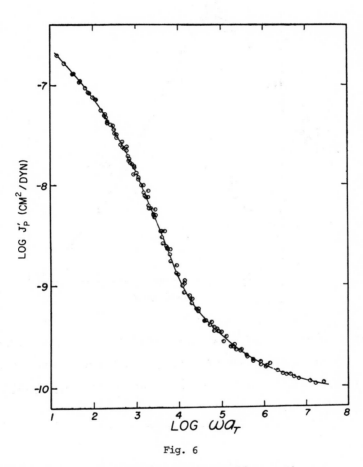

Fig. 6

Master curve for the dynamic shear compliance J' as a
function of reduced frequency for polyvinyl acetate.
Reference temperature is 75°C. [Reprinted from Williams
and Ferry, <u>J. Colloid Sci</u>., 9, 479 (1954).]

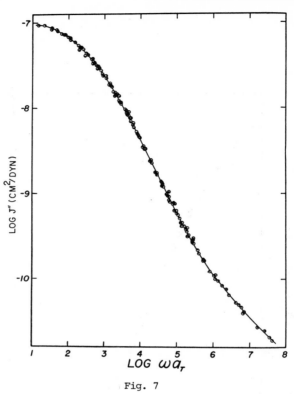

Fig. 7

Master curve for the loss compliance J" of polyvinyl acetate
as a function of reduced frequency. Reference temperature
is 75 °C. [Reprinted from Williams and Ferry, J. Colloid Sci.,
9, 479 (1954).]

except at very low frequencies. The distribution of relaxation
times H($\ln \omega$) is given approximately by

$$H(\ln \omega) \doteq \frac{d\ G'(\ln \omega)}{d\ \ln \omega} \tag{3}$$

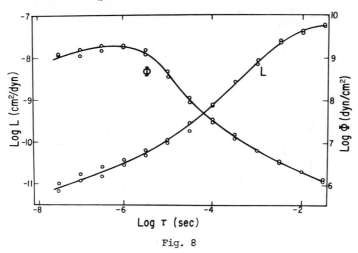

Fig. 8

Distribution of relaxation times φ and distribution of
retardation times L for polyvinyl acetate reduced to 75°C.
[Reprinted from Williams and Ferry, J. Colloid Sci., 9,
479 (1954).]

---

or

$$H(\ln\ \omega) \doteq \frac{2}{\pi}\ G''(\ln\ \omega) \tag{4}$$

where $G'(\ln\ \omega)$ and $G''(\ln\ \omega)$ are the master curves for the dynamic
shear modulus and the loss modulus as a function of the angular
frequency ω. Thus, the distribution of relaxation times is
approximately proportional to the slope of the modulus curve
on a logarithmic frequency scale. The distribution is proportional also to the damping or loss modulus G'' as a function
of frequency. If the dynamic master curves are plotted as
dynamic compliances J rather than as moduli, the distribution

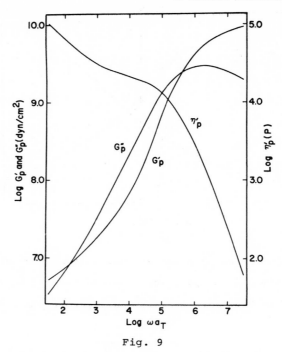

Fig. 9

Dynamic shear modulus G_P', loss modulus G_P'', and dynamic
viscosity η_P' for polyvinyl acetate as a function of reduced
frequency ωa_T. [Reprinted from Williams and Ferry,
J. Colloid Sci., 9, 479 (1954).]

of retardation times $L(\ln \omega)$ are approximately

$$L(\ln \omega) \doteq \frac{d\,J'(\ln \omega)}{d\,\ln \omega} \qquad (5)$$

or

$$L(\ln \omega) \doteq \frac{2}{\pi}\left[J''(\ln \omega) - \frac{1}{\omega\eta}\right] \simeq \frac{2}{\pi}\,J''(\ln \omega) . \qquad (6)$$

Ferry (2) reviews the numerous higher order approximations to
$H(\ln \omega)$ and $L(\ln \omega)$. In the region where viscous flow occurs,

the damping effect due to viscosity η should be subtracted
from the total damping or loss compliance J". In most
practical cases, these equations are seldom used because of the
great effort needed to construct a good master curve.

If it is necessary to convert one type of data into
another type, approximate equations have been developed which
do not require the use of distributions of relaxation or
retardation times (2, 68-71). The simplest of these equations
for converting one type of data into another are given by the
following equations. Time and angular frequency are related by

$$t = 1/\omega. \tag{7}$$

Creep can be calculated from dynamic mechanical compliance
by (2,68)

$$J(t) \doteq J'(\omega) + 0.40J''(0.40\omega) - 0.014J''(10\omega). \tag{8}$$

For each time on the creep curve, dynamic mechanical data are
required at three frequencies —ω, 0.40ω, and 10ω. Stress
relaxation G(t) can be calculated from dynamic modulus data
by a similar equation:

$$G(t) \doteq G'(\omega) - 0.40G''(0.40\omega) + 0.014G''(10\omega). \tag{9}$$

Dynamic mechanical properties can be calculated from
stress relaxation data by the equations (71)

$$G'(\omega) \doteq G(t) + 0.86[G(t) - G(2t)] \tag{10}$$

$$G''(\omega) \doteq 1.674[G(t) - G(2t)] - 0.470[G(2t) - G(4t)]$$
$$+ 0.198[G(t/2) - G(t)] + 0.620[G(t/4) - G(t/2)]. \tag{11}$$

These equations show that the dynamic modulus is greater than
the stress relaxation modulus. The equations 10 and 11 are
good approximations as long as the damping is small. For example,
the error in the dynamic modulus is less than 0.15 tan δ.
Similar approximations for dynamic compliance properties from
creep data are (69,70):

$$J'(\omega) \doteq J(t) - 0.86[J(2t) - J(t)] \qquad\qquad (12)$$

$$J'(\omega) \doteq 2J(t) - J(2t) \qquad\qquad (13)$$

$$J''(\omega) \doteq 2.12[J(t) - J(t/2)]. \qquad\qquad (14)$$

The error for $J'(\omega)$ is less than 0.15 tan δ, but the equation
for $J''(\omega)$ is a rough approximation, especially at low damping.
Schwarzl (70) has proposed another equation for estimating creep
data from dynamic compliances:

$$J(t) \doteq J'(\omega) + 0.566\ J''(\omega/2) - 0.203J''(\omega). \qquad (15)$$

This equation is a very good approximation at low damping, and
the error is less than 7.5 percent even at high damping. Creep
compliance is greater than dynamic compliance as shown by

$$J(t) \doteq (1 + 0.36\ \tan δ)J'(\omega). \qquad\qquad (16)$$

When creep can be expressed by the Nutting (72, 73) equation,
which is frequently the case, the damping can be estimated.
The Nutting equation is

$$\log ε(t) = \log K + \log σ + n \log t, \qquad\qquad (17)$$

where $ε(t)$ is the creep strain as a function of time, $σ$ is the
applied stress and K and n are constants at a given temperature.

The constant n, which can vary between zero (perfect elasticity) and 1.0 (pure Newtonian viscosity behavior), is evaluated from a double logarithmic plot of the creep and time by

$$n = \frac{d \log \varepsilon}{d \log t} .\qquad(18)$$

The damping is then often given by (73)

$$\frac{E''}{E'} \doteq \frac{\pi}{2} n.\qquad(19)$$

If the creep curve is not linear on a log-log plot of compliance versus time, it is often linear on a semilogarithmic plot of compliance versus log time. In this case the damping can be estimated from (74):

$$\frac{E''}{E'} \doteq \frac{\pi n_1}{2 \, K_1 \, \log_e 10}\qquad(20)$$

where n_1 and K_1 are constants determined from the creep curve, defined as

$$\frac{\varepsilon(t)}{\sigma_0} = K_1 + n_1 \log t\qquad(21)$$

and K_1 is a constant which at t=1 is the one second creep compliance.

A simple method of predicting the loss modulus E" from stress relaxation data has been suggested by Dunell and Tobolsky (75,76).

$$E'' \doteq \frac{-\pi}{4.606} \frac{d \, E_r(t)}{d \log t} .\qquad(22)$$

The loss modulus at any frequency can be estimated from the
slope of the stress relaxation modulus $E_r(t)$ versus time curve
by converting time to frequency ω through the relation $\omega = 1/t$.

Dynamic mechanical properties also may be expressed in terms
of complex viscosities rather than as moduli. The important
definitions and equations were given in Chapter 1. One might
anticipate that the dynamic viscosities as a function of
frequency are related to the melt viscosities as a function of
the rate of shear $\dot{\gamma}$. Such relationships were proposed by
Cox and Merz (77, 78). Viscosity data on a typical polymer
melt as a function of the rate of shear, as determined by a
rheometer such as a capillary rheometer or a plate and cone
rheometer (79), are shown in Figure 10 (3). Because of elasticity,
the slope of the shear stress versus the rate of shear curve

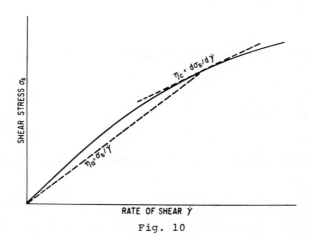

Fig. 10

Definition of apparent viscosity η_a and consistency η_c
from a typical shear stress versus rate of shear curve for
a molten polymer.

decreases with rate of shear. The viscosity as defined by the
slope of the line at any point is called the consistency η_c
while the viscosity defined by the secant is called the apparent
viscosity η_a. Both viscosities are functions of the rate of
shear, $\dot{\gamma}$. Cox and Merz extended the hypothesis of DeWitt (80)
that angular frequency ω is equivalent to rate of shear $\dot{\gamma}$ to
derive the following relations:

$$\eta_a(\dot{\gamma}) \doteq \eta^*(\omega). \tag{23}$$

$$\eta_c(\dot{\gamma}) \doteq \eta'(\omega). \tag{24}$$

$$G' \doteq \dot{\gamma}(\eta_a^2 - \eta_c^2)^{1/2}. \tag{25}$$

The complex viscosity is $\eta^*(\omega)$, and the real part of the
dynamic viscosity as a function of the angular frequency is
$\eta'(\omega)$. (See discussion and definitions in Chapter 1.) The
decrease in the viscosities and the increase in shear modulus
with increasing frequency or rate of shear are shown in
Figure 11 (78). Generally, the equivalence of η_a and η^* is
found to hold experimentally, but the other relations are not
very accurate (81, 82). These relations imply that the decrease
in viscosities is mostly a result of the development of
elasticity in the melt at high rates of deformation.

III.   Stress or Strain Amplitude Effects

    Not much work has been done on the effect of the amplitude
of the stress or strain on the dynamic mechanical properties
of unfilled polymers. Most of the investigations have been on
filled rubbers or plastics where the effects are similar to

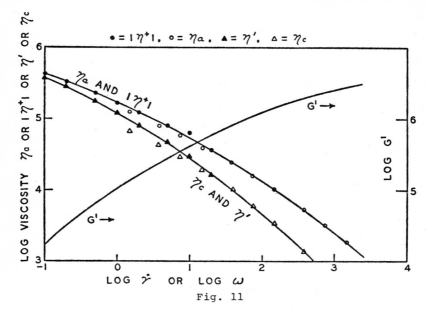

Fig. 11

Correlation of steady flow viscosity with dynamic mechanical
properties of high density polyethylene at 180°C. [Reprinted
from Cox and Merz, Spec. Tech. Publ. No. 247, Amer. Soc.
Testing Materials, 1958.]

---

but generally much greater than for unfilled polymers (74, 83-98).
Since polymers have a finite damping, the first effect generally
observed on increasing the amplitude is an increase in the
temperature of the specimen, especially at high frequencies.
Equation 12 of Chapter 1 indicates that the heat generated per
cycle is proportional to the loss modulus G" or E" and the
square of the amplitude, so the heat generated per second
becomes proportional to the product of the loss modulus, the
square of the amplitude, and the frequency. The rise in
temperature brings about changes in the modulus and damping in

a manner already described.

Even if the heat generation is too low to produce a temperature increase great enough to change the modulus and the damping, high stresses or amplitudes of deformation bring about changes in the dynamic properties. In nearly all cases, the properties are independent of amplitude up to some critical value (87-94). Above the critical stress or strain amplitude, the modulus decreases and the damping (both tan δ, and loss modulus) increase with amplitude. The critical stress is often about the same value as the stress at which the stress-strain curve becomes nonlinear. Critical values of the stress for some common polymers are (93):

Polymer	Critical Stress (psi)
Low density polyethylene	236
High density polyethylene	542
Polypropylene	885
Polystyrene	2000
Cellulose acetate	2010

The differences in dynamic mechanical properties at strains above and below the critical value of polypropylene are shown in Figure 12 (92). Sometimes the dynamic mechanical properties return to their original values when the stress is again reduced below the critical value. However, in many cases, the modulus and damping do not return to their original values, thus indicating some kind of permanent change in the polymer. With brittle polymers and high impact polyblends the change in dynamic properties often can be associated with crazing and the

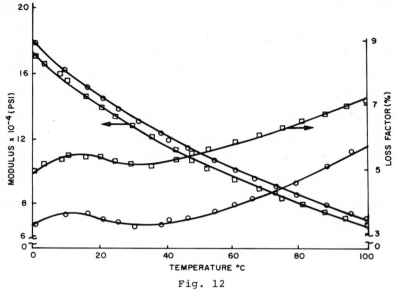

Fig. 12

Dynamic mechanical properties of polypropylene above and below the critical strain limit LLVR. ☐ Tested above LLVR, O tested below LLVR. [Reprinted from Maxwell and Heider, SPE Trans., 2, 174 (1962).]

---

formation of microscopic cracks and voids (91,99,100). With filled rubbers and other polymers, the change in dynamic properties is caused by the breaking up of filler agglomerates or the breaking of the bond between the filler and polymer phases (88-91).

Another type of amplitude dependence is found when large static loads or deformations are imposed on the polymer, and the dynamic properties are determined by superimposing small oscillatory stresses on the large static ones (91, 101-108). This type of test can be made simultaneously with a stress-strain test. In the case of crosslinked rubbers, the dynamic

modulus generally increases dramatically as the rubber is
stretched. A similar phenomenon may be observed with highly
oriented fibers, but with most rigid polymers the modulus
starts to decrease if the static load becomes too great. On
the other hand, the damping E"/E' of rubbers decreases as the
rubber is being stretched by a static load or during a stress-
strain test. The loss modulus E", however, may increase
somewhat; it is the greater increase in E' that causes E"/E'
to decrease.

IV. Thermal History

The dynamic mechanical properties of amorphous polymers
can be changed by the thermal history of the sample, but the
effects are generally much less prominent than with crystalline
polymers (109-111). Quenched-cooled polymers have greater
damping than polymers which are slowly cooled from above to
well below T_g (109). Quenching lowers T_g and the temperature
at which the damping is a maximum. Quenching also tends to
broaden the low temperature side of the damping peak (111).
Similar, but much more detailed studies, have been made by Kovacs,
Stratton, and Ferry (110). Some of their results on annealing
of polyvinyl acetate are shown in Figures 13 and 14. Annealing
at temperatures near the glass transition temperature (29°C)
after quench-cooling from the melt lowered the damping and
raised the modulus. These results are expected since the
density increases with annealing time, indicating a decrease
in free volume. Molecular mobility due to greater than
equilibrium free volume manifests itself by a lowering of the
modulus and by increased damping.

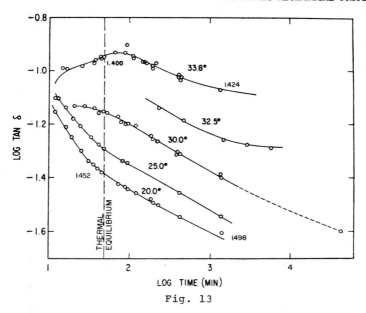

Fig. 13

Damping of polyvinyl acetate versus time in torsion pendulum
apparatus after quenching from 45 °C. Temperature of apparatus
is indicated on curves along with the frequency of oscillation.
[Reprinted from Kovacs, Stratton, and Ferry, J. Phys. Chem.,
67, 152 (1963), by permission of the copyright owner, The
American Chemical Society.]

Injection molded objects have a complex thermal history
superimposed on various orientation effects. Malpass (112)
found that such injection molded objects may contain extra
damping peaks which disappear on annealing the object.

Crosslinked or thermoset polymers may be only partially
cured before the chemical reactions are nearly stopped by
lowering the temperature. In such polymers the curing reaction

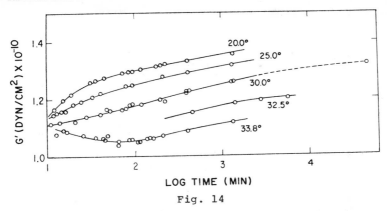

Fig. 14

Change in shear modulus G' of polyvinyl acetate with time
after quenching as in Figure 13. Temperature of apparatus
is indicated on curves. [Reprinted from Kovacs, Stratton,
and Ferry, J. Phys. Chem., 67, 152 (1963), by permission of
the copyright owner, The American Chemical Society.]

may continue very slowly for a long time, or the curing reaction
may become rapid if the polymer is heated again (27, 113, 114).
As the chemical reaction continues, T_g increases, and the
modulus tends to increase while the damping decreases.

The dynamic mechanical properties of crystalline polymers
are especially sensitive to thermal history. Slow cooling or
annealing raises the modulus and the temperature of the
crystalline alpha transition temperature compared to the values
for a quenched specimen (3,34,99,115-121). Figures 15 and 16
illustrate these effects, which are typical for many
crystalline polymers (99). The alpha transition in this case
appears to have two components with the higher temperature
component shifting more than the lower temperature component.

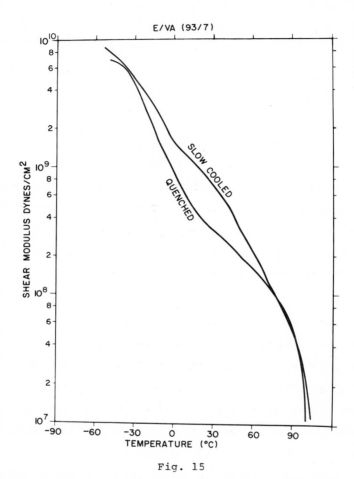

Fig. 15

Shear modulus of a polyethylene copolymer containing 7%
vinyl acetate. Quenched specimen was quenched from 160°C
into ice water. Slow cooled specimen was cooled from 160°C
to room temperature in about one hour. (Unpublished data
of L. Nielsen, Monsanto Co.)

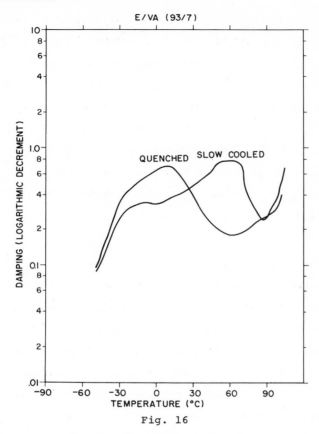

Fig. 16

Damping of a polyethylene copolymer containing 7% vinyl
acetate. Heat treatment same as that in Figure 15.
(Unpublished data of L. Nielsen, Monsanto Co.)

_____

Some polymers, such as polyethylene terephthalate and some
polyurethanes, are non-crystalline when quenched, but they
develop crystallinity on annealing or aging at temperatures
above T_g (122-124). The development of crystallinity

produces dramatic increases in the modulus above T_g as well
as changes in the damping curve. Although, in some polymers
T_g does not shift with crystallinity, in other cases, T_g is
increased (125-127). In polypropylene, quenching raises T_g
more than slow cooling. Apparently the smaller imperfect
crystallites of quenched polymer impose more restraints on the
amorphous phase than more perfect slowly formed crystallites.
A discussion of the dynamic mechanical properties of crystalline
polymers will be continued in the section on crystallinity in
this chapter.

V.   Effect of Molecular Weight

     Recalled from Chapter 2 that the length of the rubbery
plateau region above T_g in the modulus-temperature curve
depends upon the molecular weight of the polymer. The
modulus curve on a log frequency abscissa scale is similar
in shape to the reverse of temperature as the abscissa scale.
In other words, an increase in temperature is equivalent to
a decrease in frequency; this is to be expected from the
time-temperature superposition principle. Thus, on either
a log frequency scale or a temperature scale, the length of
the rubbery plateau region increases as the molecular weight
increases. It has been proposed that on a log frequency scale
that (128)

$$\text{Length of plateau} \propto 3.4 \log (M/M_e) \qquad (26)$$

where M_e is the molecular weight between entanglements as
determined from the equation for the kinetic theory of rubber
elasticity.

The damping above T_g also is strongly dependent upon
molecular weight as illustrated in Figure 17.   The value of the
damping at the minimum above T_g decreases as the molecular
weight increases (1, 129-133).   The minimum occurs near the
midpoint of the rubbery plateau region where the modulus curve
has an inflection point.   In contrast to what might be expected,
Cox, Isaksen, and Merz (129) found that the damping is a
function of the number average molecular weight rather than
the weight average molecular weight.   They also found that the
valley around the minimum in damping broadened as the ratio
of the weight to number average molecular weights increased.

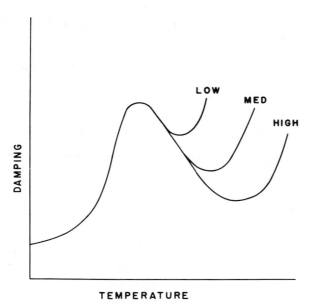

TEMPERATURE

Fig. 17

Damping versus temperature for a polymer of three different
molecular weights.

However, Oyanogi and Ferry (132) found the minimum to be
relatively insensitive to very low molecular weight polymer.
Marvin (134) developed a theory which predicts that

$$\left(\frac{G''}{G'}\right)_{min} = 1.04 \left(\frac{2 \, M_e}{\overline{M}_n}\right)^{0.80} \tag{27}.$$

The M_e used in this equation is the one calculated from the
modulus equation of the kinetic theory of rubber elasticity.
The factor 2 should be omitted if M_e is determined from the
break in the log viscosity versus molecular weight curve.
Equation 27 agrees only approximately with the experimental
data, especially if the polymer contains some material with
a molecular weight less than M_e (132).

Above T_g, dynamic mechanical data obtained as a function
of frequency can be superimposed to give master curves with
shift factors given by the W-L-F equation (66). Master curves
have been constructed for many polymers by various workers (1,135).
Typical master curves above T_g for different molecular weights
of polymethyl methacrylate are given in Figures 18 and 19 (135).
The designations on the graphs correspond to the following
molecular weights:

Polymer	M_w	M_n
MF2	342,000	224,000
MF3	270,000	188,000
MF5	197,000	146,000
MF6	158,000	139,000
MF7	116,000	98,000
MF8	96,300	71,800
MF9	63,900	52,800
MF10	45,200	37,100
MF11	35,100	25,300
MF12	28,400	18,000
MF13	11,400	9,120

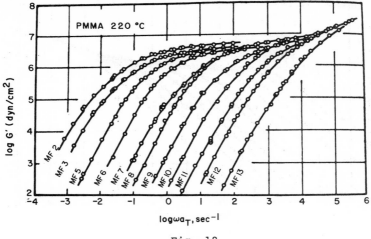

Fig. 18

Master curves of dynamic shear modulus versus reduced
frequency for different molecular weight polymethyl
methacrylates. Reference temperature is 220°C. [Reprinted
from Masuda, Kitagawa, and Onogi, Polymer J., 1, 418 (1970).]

The values of the moduli in the rubbery plateau region for both
G' and G" are essentially independent of molecular weight
because the molecular weight between entanglements is constant.
However, the plateau includes a wider range of frequencies as
the molecular weight increases. The viscosity η_0 at zero rate
of shear is given at very low frequencies ω by

$$\eta_0 = G''/\omega, \qquad \omega \to 0 \qquad (28)$$

The steady state compliance J_e^o at low frequencies is

$$J_e^o = \frac{G'}{\omega^2 \eta_0^2}, \qquad \omega \to 0 \qquad (29).$$

At temperatures below T_g, molecular weight has little,

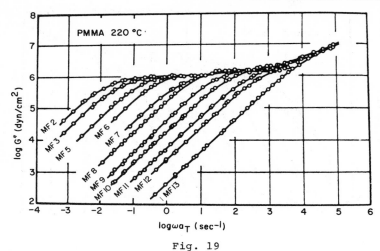

Fig. 19

Master curves for the loss modulus versus reduced frequency
for polymethyl methacrylates of different molecular weights.
Reference temperature is 220°C. [Reprinted from Masuda,
Kitagawa, and Onogi, Polymer J., 1, 418 (1970).]

if any, effect upon the dynamic mechanical properties.

VI. Effect of Crosslinking

Crosslinking has a dramatic effect on the dynamic mechanical
properties above T_g. The vulcanized rubbers are typical of
relatively low degrees of crosslinking. If the frequency of
the test is too high, the modulus does not reach an equilibrium
value, and the expected increase in modulus with degree of
crosslinking becomes partly obscured by entanglements and
imperfections such as trapped entanglements or dangling crosslinked structures (136, 137). However, the damping is a

sensitive indicator of crosslinking (138-140). At temperatures
well above T_g, the damping decreases with increasing degree of
crosslinking, as illustrated in Figure 20 where the swelling
ratio is an inverse function of the degree of crosslinking.
The measurement of the damping of a vulcanized rubber is an
extremely rapid method of determining crosslinking compared to
a swelling test, once a calibration curve has been constructed
for the given type of polymer.

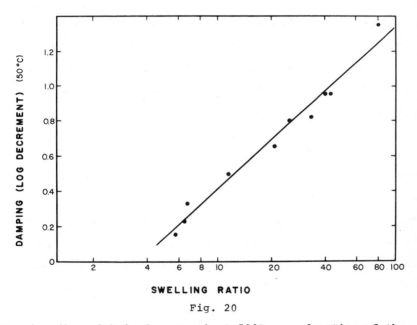

SWELLING RATIO

Fig. 20

Damping (logarithmic decrement) at 50°C as a function of the
swelling ratio for crosslinked SBR rubber. Benzene was the
solvent for the swelling tests. [Reprinted from Nielsen,
J. Macromol. Sci., C3, 69 (1969), Marcel Dekker, Inc, New York.]

According to the kinetic theory of rubber elasticity (141-144) the equilibrium shear modulus is given by

$$G = \left(\frac{\overline{r^2}}{\overline{r_0^2}}\right) \frac{\rho RT}{M_c} \left(1 - \frac{2 M_c}{\overline{M}_n}\right) \tag{30}$$

where ρ is the density of the polymer, M_c is the molecular weight between crosslinks, $\overline{M}_n$ is the number average molecular weight of the uncrosslinked polymer, R is the gas constant, and T is the temperature in degrees Kelvin. The ratio of the mean-square distance between network junctures to the mean-square end-to-end distance of network chains in free space is $\overline{r^2}/\overline{r_0^2}$; this ratio is generally near 1.0. The term $2M_c/\overline{M}_n$ corrects for chain ends not effectively tied into the network, and except for very low degrees of crosslinking, it can be neglected. Equation 30 then becomes

$$G \doteq \frac{\rho RT}{M_c} \doteq nRT \doteq 2 C_x RT \tag{31}$$

where n is the number of moles of network chains per unit volume of polymer, and C_x is the number of moles of tetrafunctional crosslinking agent per unit volume of polymer. The agreement between theory and experiment is good at low degrees of crosslinking such as found in vulcanized rubbers. However, the equations of the kinetic theory of rubber predict moduli far too small for extremely highly crosslinked materials (145-146). Epoxies and the even more highly cross-linked phenol-formaldehyde resins are examples of polymers which are much more highly crosslinked than normal rubbers. Nielsen (146) has proposed an empirical equation which agrees much better than equation 30 with the experimental results at very high degrees of crosslinking:

$$\log_{10} G \doteq 7.0 + \frac{293\rho}{M_c} . \tag{32}$$

More recently another equation has been found which appears to be more accurate than equation 32 for most polymers crosslinked by divinyl monomers (99). The equation does not hold well for most epoxies.

$$\log_{10} G \doteq 7.00 + 23.6 \; \rho X_x . \tag{33}$$

The shear modulus G is in dynes/cm^2, ρ is the density of the polymer, and X_x is approximately the mole fraction of cross-linked atoms. X_x is defined exactly by $X_x = M_x/M_c$ where M_c is the total molecular weight of repeat unit between crosslinks and M_x is the molecular weight of the trifunctional crosslinked atoms plus their attached hydrogen atoms. Methyl or other side groups on the crosslinked atoms are not included in the calculation of M_x. Generally $M_x = 26$ for polymers crosslinked by divinyl and similar monomers containing two crosslinked carbon atoms. Figures 21-23 are typical of how the dynamic mechanical properties change with high degrees of crosslinking (140,147). The modulus above T_g dramatically increases, T_g shifts to higher temperatures, and the damping peak becomes very broad (113, 140, 145, 147-155). At extremely high crosslinking, the glass transition either disappears, or it is shifted to such a high temperature that the polymer decomposes before reaching T_g. It is generally assumed that the broadening of the transition region is due to a distribution in the molecular weight between crosslinks or some other kind of heterogeneity in the network

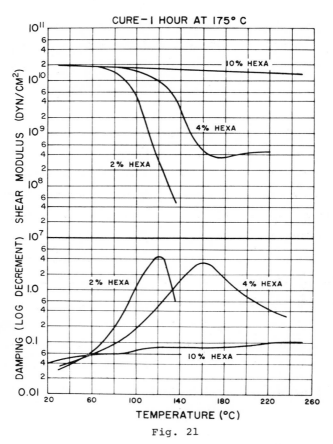

Fig. 21

Dynamic mechanical properties of a phenol-formaldehyde resin
(novolac) crosslinked with various amounts of hexamethylene-
tetramine (hexa). [Reprinted from Drumm, Dodge, and Nielsen,
Ind. Eng. Chem., 48, 76 (1956) with permission of the
American Chemical Society.]

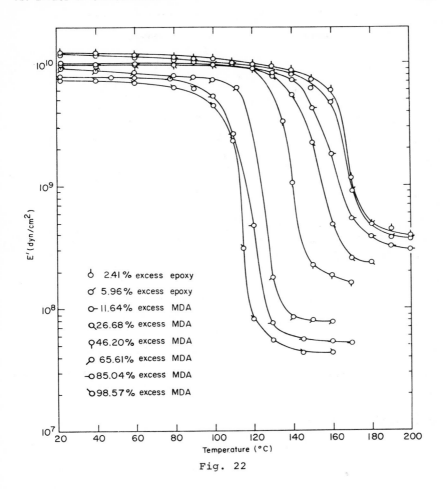

Fig. 22

Dynamic Young's modulus of epoxy resins with increasing
degree of crosslinking. Crosslinking increases as the
ratio of the components, MDA and epoxy, approach the stoichiometric value. [Reprinted from Murayama and Bell, J. Polymer
Sci., A2, 8, 437 (1970).]

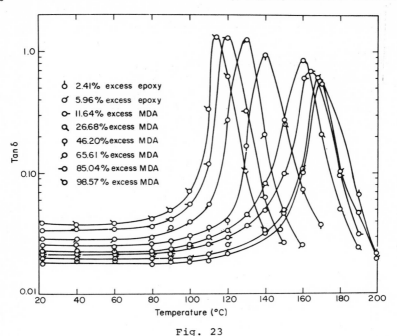

Fig. 23

Damping of epoxy resins with increasing degree of crosslinking.
Crosslinking increases as the ratio of the components approaches
the stoichiometric value. [Reprinted from Murayama and Bell,
J. Polymer Sci., A2, 8, 437 (1970).]

structure (148). However, Mason (152) believes the broadening
is due to a broadening in the distribution of free volume
between monomeric units.

The crosslinking or curing reaction in thermosetting polymers,
such as epoxies and phenol-formaldehyde resins, slows down
drastically at T_g and below even though the chemical reactions
are not complete (113, 146, 149). (T_g may appear to be higher
than the curing temperature but this is generally due to heat

build-up from the chemical reaction which raises the temperature above the measured curing temperature.) The curing reaction stops because molecular motions and diffusion, which are essential for reactions to occur, cease below T_g. If at some later time, the temperature is raised above T_g, the curing reaction will continue, and T_g will gradually increase until the reaction is completed or T_g again increases to the reaction temperature (113, 149). If the curing reaction continues to occur during the course of a dynamic test, the transition will appear falsely to be extremely broad because the T_g tends to increase as the test temperature increases (113). If the test is repeated a second time on the same specimen, the transition region will be at a higher temperature and much narrower if a crosslinking reaction occurred during the first test. Crosslinking reactions manifest themselves in another way too; the modulus will decrease with temperature in the usual manner until the reaction starts, and then the modulus will increase with temperature.

In some thermosetting systems the crosslinked network is so heterogeneous that two phases tend to appear (113, 156-158). This two-phase structure appears to be due to a microgel structure imbedded in and crosslinked to a general matrix structure. The microgel particles could develop at "hot spots" where there were initially small excesses of the crosslinking or catalyst reagent. Two-phase crosslinked polymers have a double damping peak as shown in Figure 24 (146).

VII. Effects of Crystallinity and Morphology

As explained in Chapter 2, the modulus rapidly increases

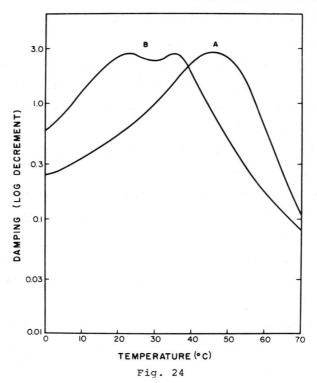

Fig. 24

Comparison of the damping of a homogeneous epoxy resin (A)
with a heterogeneous two-phase epoxy containing microgel (B)
of a similar chemical composition.   [Reprinted from Nielsen,
J. Macromol. Sci., C3, 69 (1969), Marcel Dekker, Inc., New York.]

with crystallinity because of crosslinking and filler effects
of the crystallites.   These effects, as illustrated in
Figure 25, are especially prominent between T_g and the melting
point (117).   As a first approximation, the modulus above T_g
is related to the degree of crystallinity w_c as shown in
Figure 26, which is approximated up to moderate crystallinities

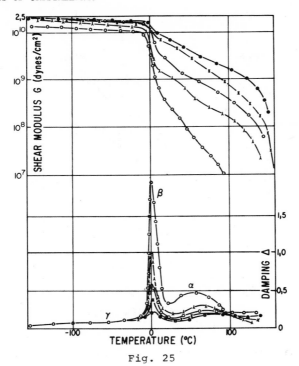

Fig. 25

Shear modulus G and damping (logarithmic decrement) of
polypropylenes as a function of degree of crystallinity.
The degree of crystallinity increases with density.

	Density	
O	0.87	($w_c \approx 0$)
⅄	0.875	
□	0.880	
X	0.894	
●	0.905	($w_c \approx 0.65$)

[From Flocke, <u>Kolloid Zeit.</u>, 180, 118 (1962), Dr. Dietrich
Steinkopff Verlag, Darmstadt, Germany.]

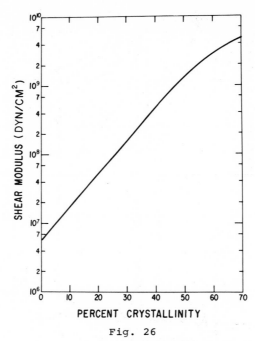

PERCENT CRYSTALLINITY

Fig. 26

Dynamic shear modulus of semicrystalline polymers as a
function of crystallinity above T_g at a frequency of about
one cycle per second.   [Reprinted from Nielsen, J. Appl.
Polym. Sci., 2, 351 (1959).]

_____

by the equation (159):

$$\log_{10} G \doteq 6.763 + 4.77 \, w_c. \tag{34}$$

This equation also may be written as

$$\log G = w_c \log G_c + (1 - w_c) \log G_a \tag{35}$$

where G_c is the modulus of the pure crystal, and G_a is the
modulus of the amorphous polymer above T_g.   This equation

implies that $G_c \doteq 3.4 \times 10^{11}$ dynes/cm^2 for polymer crystals,
and $G_a \doteq 5.7 \times 10^6$ dynes/cm^2 for the rubbery phase. Equation 35
is called the logarithmic rule of mixtures, and it is known to
hold for many types of two-phase systems in which both phases
are continuous.

The modulus not only depends upon the degree of crystallinity
but also to some extent upon the crystal morphology. For some
polymers, it has been found that the modulus is more closely
related to the specific volume of the semi-crystalline polymer
than it is to the degree of crystallinity (115, 160, 161).
For polyethylenes of any degree of crystallinity and at any
temperature between 20°C and the melting point,

$$\log_{10} G \doteq 26.671 - 16.21 \, \bar{v} \qquad\qquad (36)$$

where $\bar{v}$ is the specific volume of the polyethylene in ml/g,
and G is the shear modulus in dynes/cm^2 (115).

A number of theories have been proposed for relating the
modulus to the degree of crystallinity (162-169). The most
detailed of these theories is one by Nielsen and Stockton (166)
for crystalline copolymers. This theory predicts values of
the modulus which are somewhat low but still reasonably
accurate up to moderate degrees of crystallinity. This is
especially true if more modern equations are used for the filler
effect than the equation originally used by Nielsen and
Stockton. However, in general, the theories predict moduli
which are too low probably because the crystalline phase, as
well as the amorphous phase, is essentially continuous over
much of the intermediate crystallinity range. At least, this

is one of the implications of equation 35. At very high
degrees of crystallinity, the crystallites become the
continuous phase while the amorphous phase acts like a
dispersed phase; Bondi (168) has shown a method of calculating
the modulus as a function of w_c for this case by using the
theory of composite materials. (The moduli of various kinds
of composite materials will be discussed in detail in Chapters
7 and 8.) In any case, near the melting point where the degree
of crystallinity is changing rapidly with temperature, the
modulus decreases rapidly as the temperature increases.

The damping behavior of crystalline polymers is generally
more complex than that of amorphous polymers. Crystalline
polymers have a damping peak corresponding to the glass
transition. However, since part of the polymer is in the
crystalline state, the intensity of the damping peak is reduced.
The intensity of the damping peak often is given by the
equation (170):

$$\frac{G''}{G'} = w_c \left(\frac{G''}{G'}\right)_c + (1 - w_c) \left(\frac{G''}{G'}\right)_a \tag{37}$$

where the subscripts a and c refer to the contributions of the
pure crystalline and amorphous phases, respectively. Since
the damping mostly is due to the amorphous phase in general,
the damping equation for the maximum in the damping peak
simplifies to

$$\frac{G''}{G'} \doteq (1 - w_c) \left(\frac{G''}{G'}\right)_a . \tag{38}$$

In addition to a damping peak related to the glass transition, crystalline polymers generally show at least one or two peaks which are related to the crystalline phase. One such peak (often called the alpha transition) is generally a broad damping peak between T_g and the melting point. (The nomenclature for transitions is somewhat confusing. For amorphous polymers, the alpha transition is the glass transition. However, the alpha transition is usually between the melting point and T_g for crystalline polymers, and the beta transition becomes the glass transition.) Sometimes another crystalline peak occurs at cryogenic temperatures (29, 171-176). The damping-temperature curve of a typical crystalline polymer is shown in Figure 25. Although a great deal of speculation has been made on the nature of these crystalline damping peaks, their origin is still largely unknown. The temperature and intensity of these peaks, especially the alpha transition, change with the degree of crystallinity and with morphological changes resulting from heat treatments and orientation (115, 117, 177-188).

The α-transition in polyethylene and some other polymers can be shifted in temperature by heat treatments as shown in Figure 16 (99). The α-transition is shifted to higher temperatures by high temperature annealing and to lower temperatures by quenching. Highly crystalline unbranched polyethylene has an α-transition near 100°C while less crystalline branched polyethylene has a transition closer to 60°C. The alpha transition often appears to be made up of two transitions. The temperature of the α-transition correlates with the length of the folds in the crystals. There also is a

correlation with the melting point of a linear paraffin crystal
made up of hydrocarbon chains equal in length to the fold
length in polyethylene crystallites (179,189). The longer the
paraffin chain the higher is its melting point. The exact
mechanism giving rise to the α-transition is still unclear.
However, there is some evidence that it may be the result of
shearing of the amorphous-like material sandwiched between
crystalline lamellae (180,185). Another hypothesis is that
the α-transition is associated with the temperature at which
the polymer chains may rotate about their longitudinal axis in
the crystal (182, 190).

Highly crystalline polymers tend to have a spherulitic type
of morphology in which the crystallization progresses in all
directions from nucleation centers until the spherulites
impinge upon each other. Surfaces such as the surfaces of
molds may act as nucleation sources for crystallization. If
the surface has many nucleation points, the crystals are
forced to grow perpendicular to the surface instead of in the
usual spherulitic manner. This surface type of crystallization
is known as transcrystallinity (191-194). For nylons,
polyethylene, and some other crystalline polymers the modulus
of transcrystalline material is several times as great as that
of the spherulitic material. Since oriented crystalline
polymers are very anisotropic, undoubtedly some of the moduli
must be lower than the one measured in the direction parallel
to the surface. As might be expected, different mold surfaces
vary in their ability to produce transcrystalline material (192).
Part of this difference must be related to the ability of the
surface to act as a source of nucleation, but part of the effect

also may be related to the thermal conductivity of the material
used for the mold.

VIII.   Effects of Plasticizers and Copolymerization

Plasticizers are added to a polymer primarily for two
reasons: 1. To lower T_g so that a rigid polymer becomes soft
and rubbery.   2. To make the polymer more easily processed.
However, in addition to shifting the modulus curves and damping
peaks to lower temperatures, plasticizers generally broaden
the transition region as illustrated in Figures 27, 28 (7).
The damping peak is broader for plasticizers that are poor
solvents for the polymer than it is for good solvents (195, 196).
Thus, a poor solvent such as dioctyl phthalate gives a broader
and lower peak than a good solvent such as diethyl phthalate in
polyvinyl chloride (195). The damping peak reaches its maximum
width at about 40 volume percent plasticizer, and then the peak
narrows somewhat at higher plasticizer concentrations (195).
In the example shown in Figure 27, plasticizer also extends
the rubbery plateau region and lowers the value of its modulus.
The lowering of the modulus comes from the dilution of the
polymer and from the increased molecular weight between
entanglements (143). The length of the rubbery plateau region
is increased because the plasticizer lowers T_g more than it
does the melting point of the slightly crystalline polyvinyl
chloride.

Copolymerization can greatly increase the processibility of
crystalline polymers by reducing the melting point more than a
comparable amount of plasticizer would. Breaking up the polymer
chain by noncrystallizable monomeric units allows only short

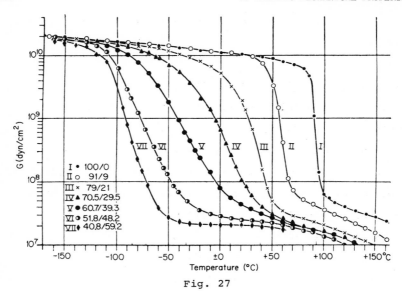

Fig. 27

Dynamic shear modulus of polyvinyl chloride plasticized with various amounts of diethylhexyl succinate plasticizer at about 1 Hz. Numbers refer to ratio of polyvinyl chloride to plasticizer. [Reprinted from Schmieder and Wolf, Kolloid Zeit., 127, 65 (1952), Dr. Dietrich Steinkopff Verlag, Darmstadt, Germany.]

---

crystalline units with low melting points to develop. The dynamic mechanical properties of copolymers are very similar to those discussed above for plasticized polymers, except that the rubbery plateau region will be shortened rather than lengthened in the case of a crystalline polymer copolymerized with a noncrystallizing comonomer.

Copolymerization can tend to broaden the damping peak, especially in many free radical copolymerizations. This is

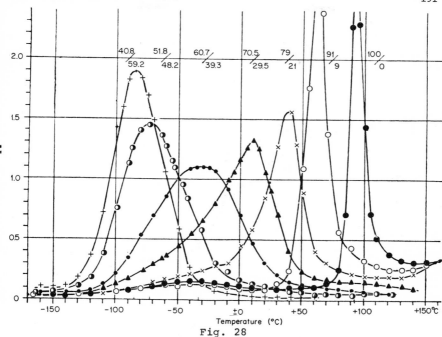

Fig. 28

Damping (logarithmic decrement) at about 1 Hz of polyvinyl
chloride plasticized with various amounts of diethylhexyl
succinate. Numbers refer to the ratio of polyvinyl chloride
to plasticizer. [Reprinted from Schmieder and Wolf,
Kolloid Zeit., 127, 65 (1952), Dr. Dietrich Steinkopff Verlag,
Darmstadt, Germany.]

---

the result of a type of chemical heterogeneity in which there
are differences in overall chemical composition from one
molecule to another (197-199). The effect is shown in Figure
29 (197). At the beginning of a polymerization, one comonomer
tends to concentrate in the copolymer more than the other
monomer. During the course of the polymerization the more

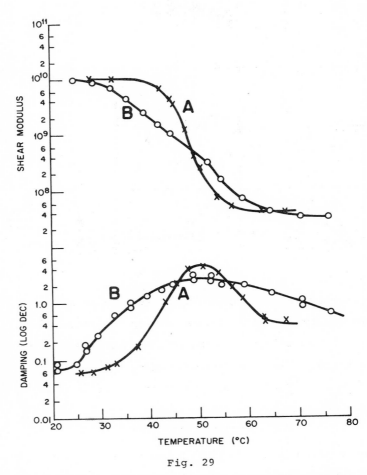

Fig. 29

Dynamic mechanical properties of vinyl chloride-methyl
acrylate copolymers. A. Homogeneous; B. Heterogeneous.
[Reprinted from Nielsen, J. Amer. Chem. Soc., 75, 1435
(1953) with permission of the copywrite owner.]

reactive monomer will be depleted in concentration, so the
copolymer molecules become enriched with the slower reacting
monomer late in the polymerization reaction. Thus, the
heterogeneous copolymer ends up with molecules which would
have a wide spread in T_g. Polymer mixtures have a strong
tendency to separate into different phases unless the components
have nearly the same solubility parameter (198-200). It can be
shown that the broadening of the damping peak results from this
tendency for insolubility rather than from the chemical
heterogeneity, per se. Mixtures of two polymers, such as polyvinyl acetate and polymethyl acrylate, which are completely
soluble in one another give a sharp damping peak even though
their glass transition temperatures are very different (198,
199, 201).

The relative efficiencies of copolymerization and plasticization
on lowering glass transition temperatures, melting points, and
degree of crystallinity are schematically shown in Figure 30.
Copolymerization is more efficient in lowering melting points
and the degree of crystallinity of crystalline polymers, but
good plasticizers are more effective in lowering T_g. About
forty percent of a comonomer will destroy all the crystallinity
of even a highly crystallizable homopolymer. But, moderately
good solvents and plasticizers at much higher concentrations
will not destroy the crystallinity of polymers such as polyethylene and polyvinyl chloride unless heated to temperatures
approaching the melting points.

Water can be considered as a plasticizer for polar polymers.
The T_g of nylons and polyvinyl alcohol is greatly reduced by

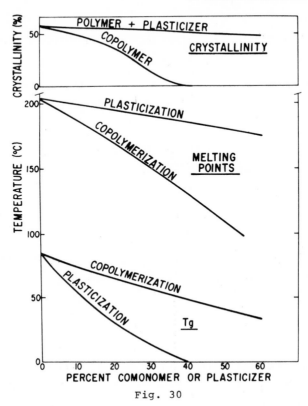

Fig. 30

The relative lowering of the degree of crystallinity, the
melting point, and the glass transition temperature by
copolymerization and by plasticization.

---

only a percent or so of water (202-207). Strong hydrogen bonds
in nylons act similar to crosslinks in raising T_g (206, 208).
Small amounts of water (about 5% or less) break these bonds
and cause an abnormally large decrease in T_g. At higher
concentrations (above about 5%), the decrease in T_g is at the
rate expected for a normal plasticizing liquid with a glass

transition temperature of -140°C (202, 209). The T_g of water is about -140°C (210, 211). In addition to its effect on T_g, water also affects the secondary glass transitions in many cases, and it also often is the cause of a new secondary glass transition in the region -50° to -100°C (122, 204, 207, 212-214).

The addition of liquids and plasticizers to polymers causes a complex series of secondary glass transition phenomena (212-223). The secondary glass transitions may be shifted up or down in temperature, they may disappear, or new damping peaks may develop. One type of phenomenon, which has been incorrectly called anti-plasticization, is quite common (224-230). Some polymers such as polycarbonates and polyvinyl chloride have large secondary glass transitions. In addition to lowering the T_g in the usual manner, many liquids and plasticizers cause the secondary transition to disappear, or at least its intensity is decreased. With the disappearance of the secondary glass transition, the modulus increases in the temperature region between the original secondary and main glass transitions, and the polymer changes from a ductile to a brittle material. These effects are illustrated in Figure 31 (226). On the molecular scale it is not known just what causes the disappearance of the secondary transition. However, it appears that some combination of molecular shape and interactions between the liquid and polymer groups causes a decrease of free volume. The molecular motions giving rise to the secondary transition cannot occur unless sufficient free volume is available in the glassy state.

Another poorly understood phenomenon often is observed on adding a liquid to a polymer. A prominent new damping peak may be introduced by the liquid even though the liquid appears to

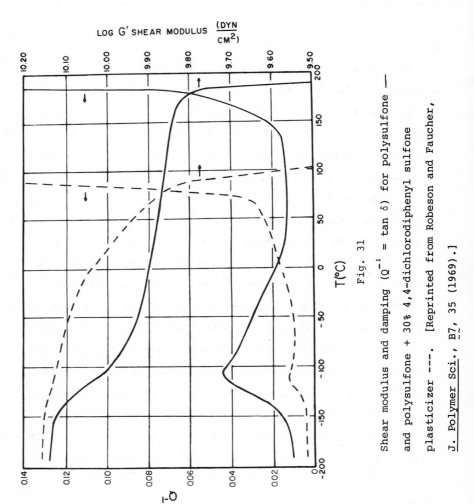

Fig. 31

Shear modulus and damping (Q^{-1} = tan δ) for polysulfone ——
and polysulfone + 30% 4,4-dichlorodiphenyl sulfone
plasticizer ----. [Reprinted from Robeson and Faucher,
J. Polymer Sci., B7, 35 (1969).]

be completely soluble in the polymer (122, 207, 213, 218, 219,
231). Sometimes this new peak is at the T_g of the pure liquid.
However, more often the new damping peak occurs at an absolute
temperature near 0.77 T_g of the pure liquid (219). This value of
0.77 T_g is where the Gibbs-DiMarzio theory predicts the true
second order transition of a glass should occur (232). It is
also the value of temperature where all the free volume of a
glass should disappear (233). This same value of 0.77 T_g is the
experimental value of the secondary transition temperature of
many simple glasses (234). It is not known what kind of an
interaction occurs between the polymer and liquid to make the
secondary transition instead of the T_g of the liquid appear.

IX. Effect of Molecular Orientation

As discussed in Chapter 2, oriented polymers are anisotropic
and have five elastic moduli. Oriented specimens may be
prepared by: 1. stretching the material while it is hot enough
to be fluid and then quenching; 2. stretching a material which
cold-draws; 3. cold-rolling of ductile materials by passing the
polymer through a mill roll. Uniaxial materials are produced
by stretching in one direction while biaxial materials are
produced by stretching or deforming the polymer the same amount
in two directions. It is difficult to prepare specimens which
are suitable for measuring some of the moduli, but at least
three of the moduli can generally be determined (235-238). The
longitudinal Young's modulus E_L for uniaxial materials can be
measured by applying a tensile stress parallel to the direction
of the polymer chains, that is, parallel to the stretching
direction, as illustrated in Figure 1 of Chapter 2. The

transverse Young's modulus E_T may be determined from the response
of the material to a stress applied at 90° to the direction of
stretching. The longitudinal transverse shear modulus G_{LT} can
be determined by torsion around an axis which is parallel to the
stretching direction. If certain conditions are fulfilled, G_{LT}
also can be approximated from tensile measurements made at 45°
to the direction of stretching (238). (See Appendix 4 for
exact relationships.) In this discussion, engineering moduli
have been used. Some of the relationships between engineering
moduli and the tensor moduli and tensor compliances are given in
Appendix 4 (235, 237, 238, 240-242).

Quantitative determinations of the degree of orientation
are difficult to obtain. The easiest qualitative measure of
orientation is generally the birefringence (64, 109, 142, 243-249).
The dichroism of certain infrared bands also can be used to
determine the degree of orientation (249-252). A similar technique
is to use the optical dichroism of polymers colored by organic
dyes (253,254). The orientation of crystallites in crystalline
polymers can be determined by x-rays (249, 251, 252, 255). For
crosslinked rubbers the orientation can be determined from the
retractive force since the change in entropy resulting from the
orientation of chain segments is the main cause of rubber
elasticity (142, 247). Therefore, the ratio of birefringence to
retractive stress for rubbers and polymer melts is often a
constant known as the stress-optical coefficient since both
phenomena are due to orientation.

The dynamic longitudinal Young's modulus E_L' generally is
greater than the Young's modulus of the unoriented polymer
(31, 109, 174, 235, 237, 238, 256-265). Typical results are

shown in Figure 32 (260). In unoriented polymers the modulus is
determined largely by intermolecular or van der Waals' forces.
However, in highly oriented polymers a tensile force in the
direction of orientation acts along the polymer chains to either
deform the much stronger covalent bond angles or possibly even
stretch covalent bonds. In very highly oriented cold-drawn fibers,
E_L can be at least a factor of ten times the modulus of the
unoriented polymer.

Moseley (258) has proposed an equation relating E_L to the
degree of orientation:

$$\text{Degree of orientation} \doteq 1 - E_U/E_L \tag{39}$$

where E_U is the Young's modulus of the unoriented polymer.

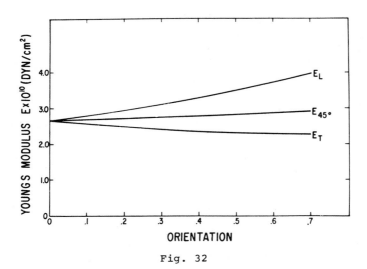

Fig. 32

Elastic moduli of polycarbonate as a function of orientation.
[Modified from Robertson and Buenker, J. Polymer Sci., A2,
4889 (1964).]

Morgan (259) finds that the degree of orientation measured by
this method agrees with that obtained from birefringence
measurements. An equation relating the moduli of anisotropic
materials to that of the unoriented polymer has been given
by Hennig (261):

$$\frac{3}{E_U} \doteq \frac{1}{E_L} + \frac{2}{E_T} \tag{40}$$

where E_T is the transverse Young's modulus.

The transverse Young's modulus E_T is generally less than the
modulus of the unoriented material (238, 260, 261, 264, 265). The
decrease in E_T due to orientation is generally much less than
the increase in E_L because both E_T and the modulus of the
unoriented material are due largely to intermolecular forces.
However, for brittle polymers such as polystyrene, E_T may appear
to be much less than that of the unoriented polymer (266). It
is believed that in such cases the low modulus is only apparent
and not real because of the ease with which cracks can propogate
parallel to the oriented molecules. It is extremely difficult
to prepare specimens which are free of cracks so that the true
modulus can be measured. Also, as a result of unwanted microscopic
cracks which are stress concentrators, the transverse strength
as well as the transverse Young's modulus is low for brittle
polymers. Orientation effects on E_L and E_T for crystalline and
amorphous polymers are very similar. However, in some crystalline
polymers above the crystalline α-transition temperature, E_T
becomes larger than E_L as illustrated in Figure 33 (264). A
possible explanation of this effect is based upon the hypothesis
that above the α-transition temperature the polymer chains

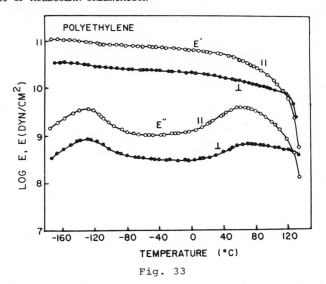

Fig. 33

Real and imaginary Young's moduli of oriented polyethylene
as a function of temperature. Measurements are shown both
parallel || and perpendicular ⊥ to the direction of
orientation. [Reprinted from Takayanagi, Imada, and
Kajiyama, J. Polymer Sci., C15, 263 (1966).]

become free to rotate about their longitudinal axis in the
crystallites (177, 270, 271). This ability to relieve a
longitudinal stress would drastically lower the longitudinal
Young's modulus, but there would be little effect upon the
transverse modulus.

The longitudinal-transverse shear modulus G_{LT} is greater than
the shear modulus of the unoriented polymer (236, 237, 239, 267, 268).
However, the increase in G_{LT} with orientation is generally less
than the increase in E_L. As shown in Figure 1 of Chapter 2, the
type of deformation used to measure G_{LT} applies forces along the

polymer chains so that the covalent bond forces begin to become
more important than in the unoriented material.

The other elastic moduli of anisotropic polymers, such as
the transverse shear modulus G_{TT} and the Poisson's ratios, have
been measured on only a few polymers (235, 237, 269, 276-279).
The transverse shear modulus is expected to be lower than the
isotropic shear modulus because the intramolecular covalent
forces become even less important than normal.

The effect of orientation on mechanical damping is not as
clearly understood as the effects on the moduli, and the
experimental results are often contradictory. For instance, in
the case of polystyrene, Nielsen and Buchdahl (109) found that
orientation increased E''/E' slightly in the longitudinal
direction. The increase may not have been due to orientation
but to an increase in free volume as a result of the quench-
cooling of the oriented specimens. Frosini and Woodward (267)
reported that orientation decreases G''/G' at cryogenic temperatures
while Armeniades, Baer, and Rieke (268) found that G''/G' is
essentially unchanged by orientation. Orientation increases
E''/E' in the longitudinal direction and decreases it in the
transverse direction for drawn polyacrylonitrile films (272).
Small amounts of orientation increase the damping of ABS polymers
(273). The low temperature γ-transition (a secondary transition)
at 210°K in polyethylene terephthalate is believed to be due to the
amorphous phase; orientation greatly reduces the intensity of
this damping peak as measured by G''/G' (239, 267). The effects
of measuring the dynamic shear properties at different angles
with respect to the orientation are illustrated in Figure 34 (239).
The shear modulus measured at 45° is higher than the moduli

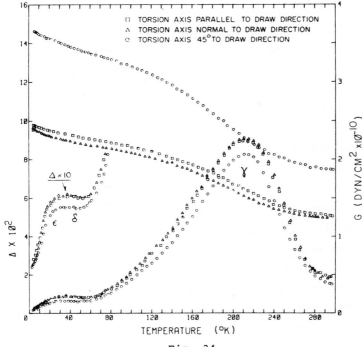

Fig. 34

Dynamic shear moduli and damping (logarithmic decrement) of oriented polyethylene terephthalate with torsion at 0°, 45°, and 90° to the stretching direction. [Reprinted from Armeniades and Baer, J. Polymer Sci., A2, 9, 1345 (1971).]

measured at 0° and 90°. The 45° measurements have a strong longitudinal Young's modulus component as shown in Appendix 4. The 0° modulus is essentially the longitudinal transverse shear modulus G_{LT}. The 90° modulus is also essentially G_{LT}, but it also has a small G_{TT} component, so the 90° shear modulus is slightly smaller than the 0° value.

With crystallizable polymers the damping behavior is further

complicated by changes in crystallinity during the orientation
process. Aligning the molecules by hot stretching or cold-drawing
increases the ease of crystallization, so an amorphous unoriented
polymer may be compared with a crystalline oriented material,
and this fact may be ignored by or unknown to the experimenter.
However, the degree of orientation is generally a more important
variable than the degree of crystallization in modifying the
dynamic mechanical properties (31, 256). Often the combined
effects of orientation and crystallization are to shift T_g to
higher temperatures and to decrease the intensity of the damping
peak associated with T_g (31, 256, 262).

Orientation produces a bewildering number of changes on the
secondary transitions of polymers. Cold-drawing lowers the
temperature of the α-transition, which is above room temperature,
in polyethylene (236, 238, 274). This lowering of the transition
temperature may be associated with the partial breaking up of
crystallites by the cold-drawing process. For the α-transition in
polyethylene, E''/E' is greater in the longitudinal direction than
in the transverse direction (238, 275). However, it has been
reported that G''/G' is greater in the transverse direction than
in the longitudinal direction for nylon, and other crystalline
polymers as well as for polyethylene (236), but this result is
contradicted by other data (238, 275). For low density polyethylene, the order of E''/E' as a function of angle for the
β-transition near $-25°C$ and the γ-transition near $-110°C$ is:

$$(E''/E')_{45°} > (E''/E')_{0°} > (E''/E')_{90°} \qquad (\beta\text{-transition})$$

and $\qquad (E''/E')_{0°} > (E''/E')_{90°} > (E''/E')_{45°} \qquad (\gamma\text{-transition}).$

The 45° modulus corresponds roughly to the value for the
longitudinal-transverse shear modulus while the 0° and the 90°
values are for the longitudinal and the transverse values,
respectively. The β-transition in polyethylene is generally
considered to be due to the amorphous phase. It has been
suggested that this transition arises from shear of the amorphous-
like polymer between crystalline lamellae (180, 275). The
secondary transitions in polymers will be discussed in more
detail in a later section.

X. Effect of Strength of Intermolecular Forces

A number of structural factors have been discussed which
dramatically affect the value of the elastic moduli and other
properties above T_g. However, most of these factors have very
little effect on the modulus below T_g. The modulus in the
glassy state is determined primarily by the strength of intermolecular forces and not by the strength of the covalent bonds
of the polymer chain. An exception is the longitudinal Young's
modulus of highly oriented materials such as in fibers where
applied forces do act primarily along the polymer chains. However,
even with fibers, the transverse Young's modulus and the shear
modulus are largely determined by the intermolecular forces or
London-van der Waals' forces. These forces are related to the
cohesive energy density of the polymer, so the modulus is
expected to increase with cohesive energy density (144, 265, 280).

An equation relating the bulk modulus B at 0°K to the cohesive
energy density δ^2 has been proposed by Tobolsky (144):

$$B \doteq 8.04 \; \delta^2 \tag{41}$$

where δ is the solubility parameter, δ^2 is the cohesive energy density in ergs/cm^3, and B has the units of dynes/cm^2. (To convert δ^2 in calories/cm^3 to ergs/cm^3, multiply by 4.186 x 10^7.) Shito and Sato (280) have used this same equation with Young's modulus replacing the bulk modulus. The data of Holliday and White (265) give an empirical equation for Young's modulus E, which is

$$E \doteq 13.3 \ \delta^2 \ . \tag{42}$$

Data on polystyrene can be used to give some indication of the accuracy of equations 41 and 42. Young's modulus at 25°C is 3.5 x 10^{10} dynes/cm^2, and at 4°K the modulus is 5.8 x 10^{10}. Equation 41 gives a modulus of 2.8 x 10^{10} dynes/cm^2 while equation 42 predicts 4.65 x 10^{10}. Table 3 indicates that in going from one kind of polymer to another, the correlation between modulus and cohesive energy density is not very good (174, 281). The way the polymer chains pack is important also.

The intermolecular bonds include dispersion forces, dipole-dipole interactions, hydrogen bonding, and electrostatic bonding. Since most organic polymers have only the relatively weak dispersion and dipolar forces, their moduli in the glassy state are all similar. Strongly polar polymers with a lot of hydrogen bonding such as polyvinyl alcohol, and polyacrylic acid should have somewhat higher moduli. Polyelectrolytes such as poly(sodium acrylate) with strong electrostatic bonding should have the highest moduli (282-285). This hypothesis is verified by the data in Figure 35 and Table 4 where polystyrene, polyacrylic acid, and poly(zinc acrylate) are compared (284). The polar, hydrogen-

Table 3

Cryogenic Young's Modulus and Cohesive Energy Density

Polymer	Cohesive Energy Density (Cal/cm^3)	Young's Modulus at 4°K $(Dynes/cm^2)$
Polyethylene	62.4	10.3×10^{10}
Polystyrene	82.8	5.8×10^{10}
Polyvinyl acetate	88.4	5.5×10^{10}
Polymethyl methacrylate	88.4	7.8×10^{10}
Polyvinyl chloride	90.2	6.8×10^{10}
Polypropylene	86.5	7.5×10^{10}
Polytetrafluoroethylene	38.4	6.0×10^{10}
Nylon 66	185.0	9.2×10^{10}
Polyethylene terephthalate	114.5	5.0×10^{10}
Polyisobutylene	61.3	7.1×10^{10}
Polyisoprene (cis)	65.2	5.6×10^{10}
Polybutadiene (trans)	70.5	9.4×10^{10}
Polybutadiene (cis)	70.5	8.7×10^{10}

bonded polyacrylic acid has a glass transition about 27°C higher
than the nonpolar polystyrene and 120°C higher than polymethyl
acrylate. The zinc salt of polyacrylic acid, which is expected
to have electrostatic bonding, has a transition of over 400°C
if one exists; on heating, the polymer eventually decomposes
without ever softening. The sodium salt of polyacrylic acid
has a T_g of 251°C (285). Its value is less than that of the zinc
salt because of the smaller electrostatic charge of the sodium

Table 4

Effect of Intermolecular Forces on T_g and Shear Modulus

Polymer	T_g (°C)	Shear Modulus at 25°C (Dynes/cm^2)
Polystyrene	100	1.25×10^{10}
Polyacrylic acid	127	3.0×10^{10}
Poly(zinc acrylate)	> 400	6.55×10^{10}

ion. It has been proposed that the T_g of polyelectrolyte polymers is determined by the electrostatic charge q and the distance d between the anion and the cation according to the equation (285):

$$T_g = K_1 (q/d) + K_2 . \qquad (43)$$

K_1 and K_2 are empirical constants. Hydrogen bonding or polarity increases the modulus of polyacrylic acid by a factor of about 2.3 over that of polystyrene. The zinc salt has a modulus 5.2 times that of polystyrene. This is the highest modulus ever reported for an unoriented organic polymer at room temperature. Even at 300°C the polymeric salt has a modulus about three times the value for polystyrene at room temperature. The zinc salt acts very similarly to very highly crosslinked thermoset polymers in which molecular motion is so restricted that no glass transition is observed.

XI. Polyblends, Block, and Graft Polymers

The theory of the modulus of two-phase polymer systems will be discussed in detail in Chapter 7. Experimental values

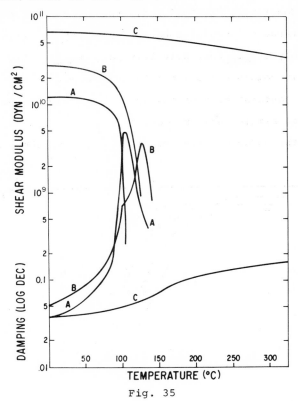

Fig. 35

Dynamic mechanical properties at about 1 cycle/second of:
A. Polystyrene; B.Polyacrylic acid copolymer (94% acrylic
acid - 6% 2-ethyl hexyl acrylate); C. Zinc salt of polyacrylic acid copolymer. [Reprinted fron Nielsen, _Polymer
Eng. Sci._, 9, 356 (1969).]

of both the modulus and damping of such materials will be
discussed in the same chapter.

A few polymeric mixtures are compatible and form one-phase
systems (197-199, 201, 248). However, most mixtures of polymers
form two phases. Typical modulus-temperature curves have been

shown in Chapter 2, Figure 8. Figures 36, 37 and 38 show the
complete range of modulus behavior from complete solubility of
the two polymers to poor solubility or compatibility and on to
essentially complete insolubility to give two phases (248).
Figure 36 contains data on mixtures of two styrene-butadiene
polymers of similar styrene content (16% and 23.5 %). The
break in the modulus curves remains steep, and the modulus is

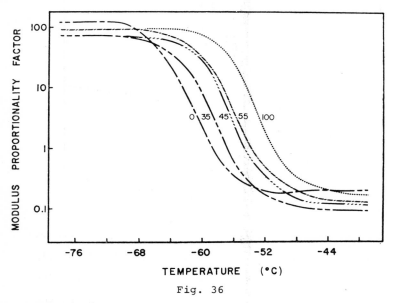

Fig. 36

The modulus proportionality factor or the relative elastic
modulus of mixtures of two styrene-butadiene copolymers of
similar styrene content (16% and 23.5%). Numbers on the
curves refer to the percent of the copolymer with the
higher styrene content in the mixture. [Reprinted from
Livingston and Brown, Proc. 5th Internat. Congr. Rheol., 4,
25 (1970).]

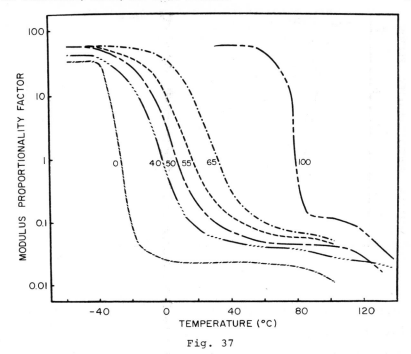

Fig. 37

Relative elastic modulus of mixtures of two styrene-butadiene
copolymers containing 37.5% and 50.0% styrene. Numbers on
the curves refer to the percent of the copolymer with the
higher styrene content. [Reprinted from Livingston and
Brown, Proc. 5th Internat. Congr. Rheol., 4, 25 (1970).]

---

just shifted on the temperature scale in proportion to the
relative concentration of the two copolymers. Figure 37 shows
the results of mixing two styrene-butadiene copolymers which
have a greater difference in styrene content (37.5% and 50.0%).
Now, the break in the modulus curves near T_g is not so steep as
the compatibility or solubility of the two copolymers is reduced.
Figure 38 shows data on mixtures of two styrene-butadiene

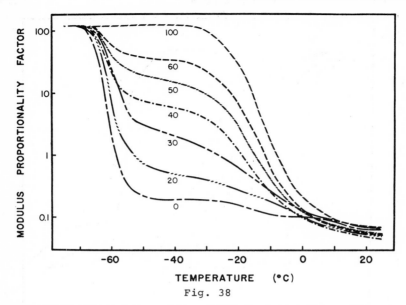

Fig. 38

Relative elastic modulus of mixtures of two styrene-butadiene
copolymers of very different styrene content (16% and 50.0%).
Numbers on the curves refer to the percent of the copolymer
with the higher styrene content. [Reprinted from Livingston
and Brown, <u>Proc. 5th Internat. Congr. Rheol.</u>, <u>4</u>, 25 (1970).]

copolymers which are very different in styrene content (16%
and 50.0%). The polymers are now insoluble in one another and
form two phases. The two steps of the modulus-temperature
curve are characteristic of immiscible two-phase systems. As
might be expected, the damping-temperature curve of two-phase
systems shows two peaks; each peak is characteristic of the
glass transition temperature of one of the components. Figure 39
shows a typical example (286). The magnitude of the peaks is
more or less characteristic of the relative concentrations of
the two components and whether or not the phases are dispersed

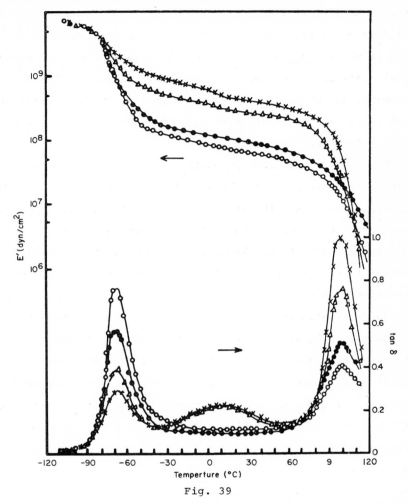

Fig. 39

Dynamic mechanical properties of a 30% styrene (MW = 15100 for
each block) styrene-butadiene-styrene block polymer cast from
different solvents which change the relative amounts of
continuous and dispersed phases.   X = methyl ethyl ketone, △ =
ethyl acetate, ● = toluene, O = carbon tetrachloride.   [Reprinted
from Miyamoto, Kodama, and Shibayama, J. Polymer Sci., A2, 8,
2095 (1970).]

or continuous (286-288). For instance, at a given concentration, G''/G' is generally greater in the higher temperature damping peak if the polymer with the higher T_g is the continuous phase (286). All two-phase polymeric systems (polyblends, block polymers, and graft polymers) are so similar in their behavior that it is extremely difficult in general to tell them apart by dynamic mechanical tests alone.

The dynamic mechanical properties of a given system can be changed by casting the polyblend, block, or graft polymer from different solvents (286, 289, 290). Typical data are shown in Figure 39 for a block polymer of styrene and butadiene. Polystyrene tends to be the more continuous phase when the solvent is relatively better for polystyrene than for poly-butadiene. This is to be expected since good solvents expand the polymer molecules while poor solvents cause the polymer chains to contract into tight coils. By freeze-drying to remove the solvent, it is sometimes possible to produce a metastable condition in which a mixture of two polymers is so intimately mixed that the mixture appears to be a single phase system with only one damping peak (289). By holding such mixtures above their highest T_g for a time the polymers again separate into two phases and show the expected two damping peaks. Some of the curves in Figure 39 show indications of an intermediate damping peak which may be characteristic of a small amount of material so intimately mixed on a molecular scale that it behaves as a single phase.

Since two-phase polymeric materials will be discussed again in Chapter 7 after the required theory of composite materials has been presented, only a brief tabulation of some of the

papers on these materials will be given at this point. In
Table 5 are given the type of system and the kinds of polymers
involved.

XII. Secondary Glass Transitions

   Most polymers have one or more damping peaks in addition to
the peak associated with the main glass transition. Some of these
peaks are associated with the crystalline phase and have been
discussed in a previous section. However, most of the damping
peaks are due to the amorphous phase and occur at temperatures
below T_g. They are called secondary glass transitions as well
as various other terms such as beta transitions, gamma transitions,
and secondary dispersions or relaxations (3,7,171,172,175,177,
184,205,215,220,221,229,319-330).

   Above the glass transition temperature virtually all possible
motions for a polymer chain occur. Below T_g nearly all these
various kinds of motions become frozen and cannot take place.
However, in some cases a few specific types of molecular motion
can occur even in the glassy state; these specific motions give
rise to the secondary glass transitions. Thus, the secondary
transitions in most cases are caused by types of motion which
normally would be expected at the main T_g and above but which
for some reason become active at much lower temperatures.
At a given frequency, say one Hz, the maximum in the damping
peak for secondary glass transitions occurs at a characteristic
temperature T_{gg}. Secondary glass transition temperatures T_{gg}
increase with frequency in a manner similar to T_g. Since the
apparent energy of activation for secondary transitions is
much less for T_g, the shift of T_{gg} with frequency tends

Table 5

References to Some Two-Phase Polymeric Materials

Reference Number	Type of 2-phase system	Polymers
288	Polyblends	Polystyrene-SBD rubbers
291	Polyblends	Polystyrene-PVC, PVC-BD/AN Copol.
292	Polyblends	Polyvinyl acetate-PMMA, Polystyrene-polymethyl acrylate
293	Polyblends	Polystyrene & PE-rubbers
294	Polyblends	Phenolic resin-Polyvinyl butyral
295	Polyblends	Polystyrene-rubber
296	Polyblends	PMMA-polyvinyl acetate
297	Polyblends	SBR- SBR
298	Polyblends	PVC-rubbers
299	Polyblends	PVC-rubbers
289	Polyblends	PMMA-polyvinyl acetate
300	Polyblends	PS-SBR
248	Polyblends	S/BD-S/BD
301	Polyblends	Polyethyl acrylate-PMMA
198	Polyblends	Methyl methacrylate-butyl acrylate copol.
199	Polyblends	SBD Copolymers
302	Graft Polymer	Rubber on PS
290	Graft Polymer	PMMA on rubber
303	Graft Polymer	PMMA on nylon
304	Graft Polymer	PS on PE
305	Graft Polymer	PMMA on polyvinyl acetate
306	Graft Polymer	Vinyl chloride-acrylate
307	Graft polymer	PS-polybutene & PS-polyacrylonitrile
308	Interpenetrating grafts	Polyacrylate-(poly(urethane-urea)
309	Grafts and blends	PS-rubber
310	Block polymers	PS-α methyl styrene

Table 5
(Continued)

Reference Number	Type of 2 phase system	Polymers
311	Block polymers	PS-polyacrylonitrile
312	Block polymers	PS-PBD, PS-polyisoprene
313	Block polymers	PS-rubber
286	Block polymers	PS-PBD
314	Block polymers	Review of many
315	Block polymers	PS-PBD
316	Block polymers	PS-PBD
317	Grafted polyblends	PS-PBD grafts
318	Block polymer	Crystalline tere-phthalate-rubber

SBD = styrene-butadiene copolymer
PS = polystyrene
PVC = polyvinyl chloride
BD/AN = butadiene-acrylonitrile copolymer
SBR = styrene-butadiene copolymer rubber
PMMA = polymethyl methacrylate
PE = polyethylene
PBD = polybutadiene

to be greater than that of T_g. However, part of this greater frequency dependence is counterbalanced by the lower temperature. (See Table 2.)

Secondary transitions may be detected by other techniques besides dynamic mechanical measurements. Two of the more sensitive techniques are electrical measurements (dielectric loss factor) (177, 331-334) and nuclear magnetic resonance measurements (335, 336). A few secondary transitions have a magnitude great enough

to be detected by breaks in volume versus temperature curves
(334, 337, 338) or by DTA measurements (208, 334).

What is the practical importance of secondary glass
transitions? Nearly all tough ductile glassy polymers and
those with high impact strength have prominent secondary transitions (3, 172, 228). Examples include polycarbonates, cellulose
polymers, polysulfones, nylons, epoxy resins, polyethylene
terephthalate, and polyvinyl chloride. Closely associated with
ductility and high impact strength is a decreased notch
sensitivity. In very brittle polymers a scratch or a notch acts
as a stress concentrator which causes a drastic decrease in
strength. Engineers are generally reluctant to use a material
which cannot be relied upon to maintain most of its strength
even if accidently scratched or cut. Therefore, in any critical
case where an object must be able to sustain tensile loads,
it is important that the material have a low sensitivity to
notches or scratches. Some types of secondary transitions
appear to decrease notch sensitivity. Also, the increased
damping due to these transitions can be important in the
reduction of the amplitudes of resonance vibrations.

It appears that only certain types of secondary glass
transitions increase ductility and impact strength even if the
T_{gg} is well below the test temperature (339-342). Secondary
transitions due to side chains are less important than backbone
motions in increasing ductility and impact strength (342). However
some T_{gg} due to backbone motions also are ineffective in producing
ductility (340).

The exact type of molecular motions responsible for secondary
glass transitions is known in only a few cases, but most T_{gg}

can be associated with one or more of the following general
classifications:

1. Side group motions such as rotations, librations, torsional
   oscillations, and wagging motions.
2. Backbone chain motions of short segments or groups.
3. Backbone or side chain motions made possible by defects in
   packing or configurations in the glassy or crystalline states.
4. Association or phase separation of impurities or diluents.

   Figure 40 (220) shows G'' as a function of temperature for a
polymer which has two secondary transitions. In this case, the
T_{gg} closest to T_g is due to motions of the ester side group,
while the low temperature T_{gg} arises from some motion of the
$-CH_2-CH_2-OH$ group. (In Figure 40, G'' rather than G''/G' is plotted;
both functions give peaks at about the same temperature, but
the high temperature peak associated with T_g would be much more
prominent if G''/G' were used.) Figure 40 also shows the effect
of a diluent on the transitions. The transition due to the ester
group has disappeared and has become part of the main T_g. The
other T_{gg} due to the hydroxyethyl group has been reduced in
intensity, and a new large peak has appeared which is primarily
characteristic of the diluent. This prominent new peak is
probably related to the T_g of the diluent as a result of diluent
molecules associating with each other as they interact with the
hydroxyethyl group to suppress its normal motion in the glassy
state.

   Polymethyl methacrylate and other methacrylate esters have
secondary glass transitions as shown in Figure 41 (7,9,184,319,
323,339,343-351). In addition to very low temperature secondary
transitions, there is another T_{gg}. For polymethyl methacrylate

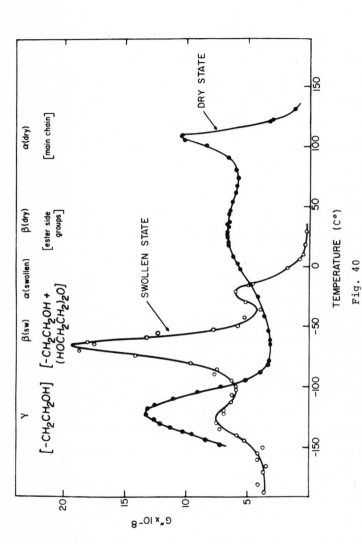

Fig. 40

Loss modulus G″ versus temperature for poly(β-hydroxyethyl methacrylate). ● Pure polymer. ○ Polymer plasticized with diethylene glycol (volume fraction 0.556). Frequency range 1 to 4.4 cps. [Reprinted from Janacek and Ferry,

J. Macromol. Sci., B5, 219 (1971). Courtesy of Marcel Dekker, Inc., New York.]

POLYMETHACRYLATES, 1 Hz

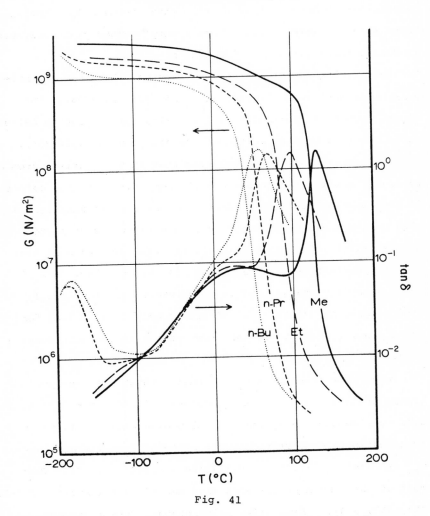

Fig. 41

Dynamic mechanical properties of four methacrylate polymers.
Me = methyl, Et = ethyl, n-Pr = n-propyl, n-Bu = n-butyl.
[Reprinted from Heijboer, Phys. of Non-Crystalline Solids,
Prins, Ed., North Holland, Amsterdam, 1965, p. 231.]

this transition at one Hz is about 40°C. High frequencies and plasticization move this transition into the main T_g. The T_{gg} below -150°C for the n-propyl and n-butyl methacrylate polymers is due to these aliphatic side chains.

Polystyrene and substituted polystyrenes have two or three secondary transitions (7, 184, 215, 325, 326, 352-356). The δ-peak occurs at about 40°K at 1 Hz. This small peak is believed to be due to a wagging motion of the phenyl group (326,356). However, it also has been suggested that this T_{gg} arises from a torsional oscillation of the phenyl group (353) or from defects in the glassy state (354). The nature of the γ-transition near -120°C is not clear; possibly it is due to traces of styrene monomer (340). The cause of the weak broad damping peak near room temperature (the β-transition) is obscure also. All of these secondary transitions in polystyrenes are very small; typical damping values of G"/G' are roughly 0.01 or less for the T_{gg} while G"/G' is of the order of one in the main damping peak.

Polymers with aliphatic side chains which are n-propyl groups or longer all have a T_{gg} between -150°C and -120°C at one cycle per second. Polymers with aliphatic chain segments in their backbone consisting of four or more CH_2 units also have a T_{gg} at -150°C to -120°C (7,9,177,184,319,350,351,357). Thus, most of the common nylons show this secondary transition (204-206, 324, 357, 358). Similarly, polyurethanes with a sequence of CH_2 units show the same T_g (122, 359-361). The exact motion of the methylene segments which is responsible for this T_{gg} is not known. It has been proposed that a crankshaft type of motion is the cause (172, 362, 363). However, this proposed mechanism is

no longer considered probable. Another proposed mechanism involves
motion of a double kink in the aliphatic chain (364).   This
transition also may be a special twisting or librational motion
of short segments of CH$_2$ units in a _trans_ configuration (365).
This motion also requires some deformation of bond angles.

The best understood secondary transition in the glassy state
is probably one due to the cyclohexyl group (320). Damping due
to this group is shown in Figure 42 for a series of copolymers

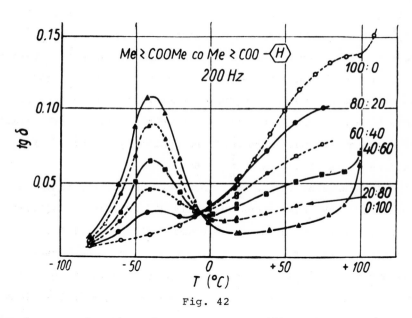

Fig. 42

Damping as a function of temperature at 200 Hz for a series
of copolymers of methyl methacrylate and cyclohexyl
methacrylate. Numbers on curves refer to the ratio of the
methyl to cyclohexyl monomers in the copolymers. [Reprinted
from Heijboer, _Kolloid Zeit._, 148, 36 (1956), Dr. Dietrich
Steinkopff Verlag, Darmstadt, Germany.]

(320-322, 366, 367). This cyclohexyl transition results from
the cyclohexyl group changing from one chair conformation to the
other chair conformation. It occurs at about -80°C at one Hz and
at -23°C at 1000 Hz. This shift in T_{gg} with frequency corresponds
to an energy of activation of 11.5 kilocalories per mole. This
T_{gg} is nearly independent of the environment of the cyclohexyl
group. Roughly the same value is found in different homopolymers
and copolymers where the group is a side chain (366). The same
T_{gg} is found even if the cyclohexyl group is in a plasticizer.
Putting the group in the backbone of a polymer shifts the T_{gg}
only 30°C above the normal temperature associated with the
cyclohexyl side group (367). Cyclic aliphatic groups containing
5, 7, or 8 carbon atoms also have a characteristic T_{gg} (321).
Six membered heterocyclic groups containing oxygen or sulfur
atoms have a damping peak at 1 Hz at -80°C, which is essentially
the same temperature as that of the cyclohexyl group (368).
Pyridine rings also show a T_{gg} (369).

Polycarbonates and polysulfones have especially prominent
secondary glass transitions (3,19,214,226,227,339,341,370,371,372).
The polycarbonates, such as the commercial bisphenol-A polycarbonate, have a T_{gg} at about -100°C at 1 Hz. The intensity of
this damping peak is high for a secondary transition; $G''/G' \doteq 0.1$.
The T_{gg} is primarily due to oscillatory or librational motions

of $-O-\overset{\overset{\displaystyle O}{\parallel}}{C}-O-$ in the carbonates and of $-\overset{\overset{\displaystyle O}{\parallel}}{\underset{\underset{\displaystyle O}{\parallel}}{S}}-$ in the sulfones. Poly-

esters such as polyethylene terephthalate have secondary
transitions which for the most part must be due to motions of
groups such as $-O-CH_2-CH_2-O-$ groups, but the very low temperature

transitions may be due to defects (123,177,185,239,256,357,373).
In polyethylene terephthalate there are several secondary
transitions; the main one is about -50°C.

Polyvinyl chloride has a broad T_{gg} around -20°C to -60°C at
one Hz (7,184,185,228-230,291,374). Because of the polar nature
of polyvinyl chloride, this transition also is easily observed
in electrical measurements of dielectric constant and loss
factor (333, 375-377). Typical dynamic mechanical data showing
both the main glass transition and the secondary transition
are given in Figure 43 (374). Although this T_{gg} has been
intensively studied, its exact nature is still unknown, but the
chlorine group must actively participate in whatever motion is
involved (229,375). It has been suggested that the T_{gg} may be
the result of stress-induced breaking of interchain hydrogen bonds
(99). This is similar to the loosening of dipole-dipole association that has been proposed by Andrews and Hammack (378).

As mentioned earlier, secondary transitions are generally
due to some molecular motion, which for some reason becomes
activated below T_g. A good indication that secondary transitions
are part of the motions normally associated with the main glass
transition can be seen by plotting the frequency at which the
damping is a maximum against the temperature at which this
maximum occurs for both T_g and T_{gg}. Such a plot is shown in
Figure 44 (333). The negative slope of these curves is proportional
to the energy of the activation for the process involved. At
high temperatures and frequencies, or for plasticized materials,
the T_{gg} (β-transition) blends in with the main T_g (α-transition).
The puzzling, largely unanswered, question is why all the possible
motions of the backbone chain do not become activated at the same

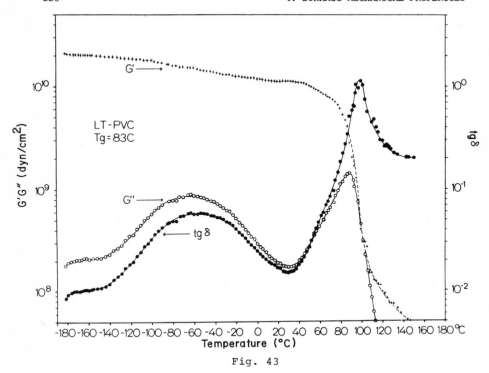

Fig. 43

Dynamic mechanical properties G', G", and tan δ for
unplasticized polyvinyl chloride as a function of temperature.
[Reprinted from Petersen and Ranby, Makromol. Chem., 133,
251 (1970).]

---

temperature.   There are several possible explanations:

1.   There are defects or inhomogeneities in molecular packing
     which leave regions of greater than normal free volume so
     that molecular motions can take place in these regions but
     not in regions of normal packing density (330).   Only certain
     molecular conformations of the backbone may be capable of
     undergoing motion in these regions of low packing density.

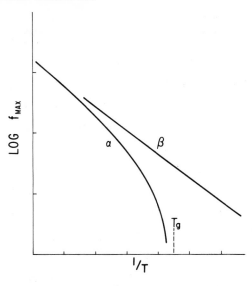

Fig. 44

Frequency at which damping is a maximum f_{max} versus the
reciprocal of the absolute temperature for a polymer with
a glass transition (α) and a secondary glass transition (β).

Only a small fraction of the repeat units participate in
these motions.

2. Large complex molecules may contain small groups ideally
    suited for rotations with little hinderance about an axis.
    The motions of these groups can be essentially decoupled from
    the motions of the remainder of the repeat unit. The
    carbonate group in bisphenol-A polycarbonate appears to be
    an example of this type of motion. Part of every repeat
    unit can participate in motions of this type while the other
    part of the repeat unit remains frozen-in. This mechanism
    for transitions is analogous to the vibrations of a series

of loosely coupled springs separated by masses of different
size. The oscillations of such a system consist of two sets
of frequencies which are known as the optical (high frequency)
and the acoustic (low frequency) modes of vibration (379).

3.   Stress-induced motions may occur. Examples may be the rupture
of hydrogen bonds between segments under stress. After such
a bond is broken, a small amount of molecular motion can
occur which makes it difficult for the same bond to reform.
As a result, a new hydrogen bond forms which initially at
least carries little, if any, stress. The net result is
energy dissipation and mechanical damping. Analogous
mechanisms take place in crystalline materials by the
motion of dislocations and slippage along certain crystallo-
graphic planes (380, 381).

Trans 1-4, polybutadiene and trans polyisoprene show unusually
strong secondary glass transitions while the cis isomers and
polyisobutylene show either no or very small transitions (365,
382). Trans polybutadiene has two large T_{gg} at about 90°K and
132°K at about 10 Hz, while trans polyisoprene has a damping
peak at 156°K. One of the damping peaks of trans polybutadiene
has been attributed to a special crankshaft motion while the
other T_{gg}, as well as the one in trans polyisoprene, may be due
to a special complex twisting motion involving rotations about
four backbone carbon atoms along with distortions of bond
angles (365). This twisting motion can take place in only a
small percent of the monomeric units which have the proper
conformation and which find themselves in the required defect
areas of lower than normal packing density. However, neither
of the proposed mechanisms can take place in cis polymers,

and so no secondary transitions are expected for them. More work is needed to clarify the exact molecular mechanism responsible for these transitions.

Cellulosic polymers such as the acetates generally have at least two or three damping peaks or transitions in addition to the main T_g (231, 337, 383). A great many other secondary transitions have been reported in the literature; a few of these include: poly(2,6-dimethyl phenylene oxide)(326,334,384,385), various polyolefins (171,386), polyoxymethylene and similar polymers (176,178,387,388), fluorine-containing polymers (10, 268,328,352,389,390), and epoxy resins (113,328,391,392). The use of torsional braid analysis for measurements of secondary transitions, curing reactions, high temperature stability, etc. has been reviewed for many polymers (393).

XIII. Summary

Dynamic mechanical tests are especially sensitive to transitions, morphological changes, and structural changes in polymers. Large damping peaks associated with various kinds of molecular motions can be correlated with glass transitions, secondary glass transitions, and sometimes with transitions associated with the crystalline state.

Types of useful information that can be obtained from dynamic mechanical tests include:

1. Glass transition temperatures and the intensity of glass transitions.

2. Temperature and intensity of many types of secondary transitions associated with both the glassy and crystalline states.

3. Melting point of crystalline polymers.

4. Number average molecular weights from the minimum in G''/G' above T_g.

5. Degree of crosslinking from G''/G' for lightly crosslinked materials and from G' for highly crosslinked thermoset polymers.

6. Completeness of curing reactions in thermoset resins.

7. Heterogeneity of crosslinks and the presence of a second microgel phase in highly crosslinked polymers.

8. Degree of crystallinity from the value of the modulus above T_g.

9. Morphological information such as the fold length in crystalline polymers from the temperature of the α-transition.

10. Heterogeneity of chemical composition in copolyemrs from the broadness of the glass transition region.

11. T_g and the solution behavior of plasticized polymers.

12. Compatibility of mixtures of polymers.

13. Composition and concentration of the components in polyblends, graft polymers, and block polymers.

14. Phase inversion in polyblends and other two-phase systems.

15. Morphology of the phases in two-phase systems.

16. Information on adhesion and on particle-particle friction in filled polymers.

17. Vibration damping and acoustic damping capability.

18. Degree of molecular orientation from modulus values.

19. Approximate predictions of creep and stress relaxation behavior.

20. Approximate qualitative stress-strain behavior as a function of temperature.

21. Estimation of impact strength of some polymers.

22. Prediction of the coefficient of rolling friction.

23. Prediction of heat distortion and softening temperatures.
     Some of these topics have not yet been discussed, but they
     will be treated in later chapters. In some of the above
     topics, accurate quantitative values are obtained, in other
     cases relative predictions are possible, while in some
     instances only qualitative predictions are possible.

XIV. Problems

1. A rubber band, which has been stretched a constant amount,
    exerts a force of 100 psi at 0°C, what will the stress be
    at 50°C?

2. The dynamic modulus changes from 10^{10} to 10^9 dynes/cm^2 in
    going through a transition. Why is the damping peak expressed
    as tan δ or G"/G' smaller than if the modulus had dropped
    to 10^7?

3. If the logarithmic rule of mixtures holds for the complex
    modulus of 2 phase systems such as crystalline polymers, show
    that the damping should be given by

    $$G"/G' = \frac{G"_1}{G'_1}\ \phi_1\ +\ \frac{G"_2}{G'_2}\ \phi_2$$

    where ϕ_1 and ϕ_2 are the volume fractions of phases 1 and 2,
    respectively. The logarithmic rule of mixtures is

    $$\log G^* = \phi_1\ \log G^*_1 + \phi_2\ \log G^*_2\ .$$

4. The melting point of toluene is -95°C. What is its expected
    T_g and secondary T_g?

5. The creep of a polymer at 25°C obeys the equation

    $$\varepsilon(t) = Kt^n\ \sigma$$

where $K = 10^{-5}$ and $n = 0.1$ if the stress is given in psi and the time in seconds. Roughly, what should G' and G''/G' be at 25°C and at a frequency of one radian per second?

6. A crystalline polymer has 3 damping peaks. How would you determine which peaks, if any, are due to the crystalline phase?

7. Polystyrene at room temperature has a damping, expressed as a logarithmic decrement, of 0.04. What is its damping expressed as: 1. E''/E', 2. specific damping capacity, 3. resilience? (See Chapter 1 for definitions.)

8. When $\sigma = \sigma_0 \sin \omega t$ is plotted on the x axis of an oscillo-scope and $\varepsilon = \varepsilon_0 \sin (\omega t - \delta)$ on the y axis, an ellipse results. Prove that the area of the ellipse is proportional to the heat dissipated per cycle and that this energy dissipated H per cycle is $H = \pi E' \varepsilon_0^2 \delta$ for small δ.

9. In the previous problem show that the maximum energy stored in the specimen is proportional to $\sigma_0^2/2E'$.

10. What is the logarithmic decrement of a free vibrating cantilever beam for the following cases? 1. The ratio of successive amplitudes is 5.0. 2. The ratio of the first amplitude to that of the fifth is 1.30.

11. The damping of a specimen in a torsion pendulum is $G''/G' = 0.01$. How many oscillations are required before the ampli-tude of the angle of twist of the pendulum becomes 10% of the initial amplitude?

12. A polymer has 2 damping peaks. One of the peaks is associated with T_g. The other peak is due to either a large secondary glass transition or an alpha transition associated with crystallinity. Show by sketches of the damping curves for these 2 possibilities how the curves

should differ. What other mechanical tests could be done to help verify which is the correct case?

13. A polymer shows 2 damping peaks. The higher temperature peak is due to the T_g of the polymer. The other peak is due to either a large secondary glass transition or due to a rubber which was added to make a polyblend. Would you expect differeces in the dynamic mechanical properties which would enable you to make a reasonable guess which is the correct case? What other kinds of tests could be made to substantiate your guess?

14. A strip of polymer is sinusoidally stretched 0.1%. If its Young's modulus is 10^{10} dynes/cm^2 and its logarithmic decrement is 0.10, how much energy is dissipated per cm^3 during each cycle? If the frequency is 10 Hz, would the temperature rise be easily detected? Assume that the heat capacity of the polymer is 0.5 cal/g and that your detection equipment will not detect temperature differences **less** than 5 °C above ambient.

15. In going through the glass transition region, the modulus of a polymer drops from 10^{10} to 10^9 dynes/cm^2. Give 3 possible reasons why the modulus did not drop to 10^7 dynes/cm^2. On the basis of only the dynamic modulus and damping data over the complete temperature range, should you be able to decide which reason is the correct one?

16. The degree of crystallinity of a copolymer decreases from 50% to 35% on raising the temperature 15 °C. Approximately how much should the shear modulus change?

17. An amorphous polymer has a molecular weight of 200,000 and a molecular weight between entanglement points of 20,000

as measured by melt viscosity tests. What is the expected
value of the damping (tan δ) at the point of minimum
damping above T_g?

18. The modulus as a function of reduced frequency of a
crystalline polymer is given in the following table. Plot
the approximate distribution of relaxation times.

Angular Frequency	Shear Modulus G' (Dynes/cm^2)
0.1	2.00×10^9
1.0	2.60×10^9
10	3.20×10^9
100	3.80×10^9
1000	4.40×10^9
10,000	5.00×10^9

19. The loss modulus as a function of reduced frequency is
given by the following table. Plot the distribution of
relaxation times.

Angular Frequency	Loss Modulus G" (Dynes/cm^2)
0.1	1.25×10^9
.3	1.39×10^9
1.0	1.65×10^9
3.0	1.92×10^9
10	2.23×10^9
30	2.51×10^9
100	2.68×10^9
300	2.72×10^9
1000	2.62×10^9
3000	2.45×10^9
10,000	2.25×10^9

XV.   References

1. J. D. Ferry, Viscoelastic Properties of Polymers, John Wiley, New York, 2nd Ed., 1969.

2. J. D. Ferry, Rheology, Vol. 2, Chap. 11, F. R. Eirich, Ed., Academic Press, New York, 1958.

3. L. E. Nielsen, Mechanical Properties of Polymers, Van Nostrand Reinhold, New York, 1962.

4. A. W. Nolle, J. Appl. Phys., 19, 753 (1948).

5. J. H. Dillon and S. D. Gehman, India Rubber World, 115, 61 (Oct. 1946).

6. R. Shaw, Rubber Chem. Tech., 22, 1045 (1949).

7. K. Schmieder & K. Wolf, Kolloid Zeit., 127, 65 (1952).

8. L. E. Nielsen, Rev. Sci. Instr., 22, 690 (1951).

9. J. Heijboer, P. Dekking, and A. J. Staverman, Proc. 2nd Int. Congr. Rheology, V. G. W. Harrison, Ed., Butterworths, London, 1954, p.123.

10. K. H. Illers and E. Jenckel, Kolloid Zeit., 160, 97 (1958).

11. K. H. Illers and E. Jenckel, J. Polymer Sci., 41, 528 (1959).

12. J. Koppelmann, Kolloid Zeit., 144, 12 (1955).

13. W. Kuhn and O. Kuenzle, Helv. Chim. Acta, 30, 839 (1947).

14. D. J. Plazek, M. N. Vrancken, and J. W. Berge, Trans. Soc. Rheology, 2, 39 (1958).

15. K. M. Sinnott, J. Appl. Phys., 29, 1433 (1958).

16. N. Tokita, J. Polymer Sci., 20, 515 (1956).

17. H. Nagerl, Kolloid Zeit., 204, 29 (1965).

18. C. J. Nederveen, Rheol. Acta, 3, 2 (1963).

19. K. H. Illers and H. Breuer, Kolloid Zeit., 176, 110 (1961).

20. F. Rodriguez, R. A. Van Brederode, & G. G. Cocks, J. Appl. Polymer Sci., 12, 2415 (1968).

21. M. E. de Morton, S. A. Lott, and D. F. Stainsby, J. Sci. Instr., 40, 441 (1963).

22. F. E. Weir, Trans. SPE, 2, 302 (1962).

23. C. J. Nederveen and C. W. van der Wal, Rheol. Acta, 6, 316 (1967).

24. T. J. Dudek and J. J. Lohr, J. Appl. Polymer Sci., 9, 3795 (1965).

25. K. Fujino, H. Kawai, and T. Horino, Textile Res. J., 25, 722 (1955).

26. A. E. Schwaneke and R. W. Nash, Rev. Sci. Instr., 40, 1450 (1969).

27. J. K. Gillham, Polymer Eng. Sci., 7, 225 (1967).

28. J. K. Gillham and M. B. Roller, Polymer Eng. Sci., 11, 295 (1971).

29. C. D. Armeniades, I. Kuriyama, J. M. Roe, & E. Baer, J. Macromol. Sci., B1, 777 (1967).

30. A. F. Lewis and J. K. Gillham, J. Appl. Polymer Sci., 7, 685 (1963).

31. J. W. Ballou and J. C. Smith, J. Appl. Phys., 20, 493 (1949).

32. M. Horio, S. Onogi, C. Nakayama, and K. Yamamoto, J. Appl. Phys., 22, 966 and 977 (1951).

33. S. Newman, J. Appl. Polymer Sci., 2, 333 (1959).

34. L. E. Nielsen, SPE. J., 16, 525 (1960).

35. D. Robinson, J. Sci. Instr., 32, 2 (1955).

36. S. Strella, ASTM Bull., No. 214, 47 (1956).

37. B. M. Chernyshev, Polymer Mech., 1, 95 (1965)(Engl. Transl.)

38. R. N. Shroff, Trans. Soc. Rheol., 12, 199 (1968).

39. W. W. Scott and R. K. Mac Crone, Rev. Sci. Instr., 39, 821 (1968).

40. G. S. Fielding-Russell and R. E. Wetton, Plast. & Polymers, 38, 179 (June, 1970).

41. R. Buchdahl, R. J. Morgan and L. E. Nielsen, Rev. Sci. Instr., 41, 1342 (1970).

42. D. E. Kline, J. Polymer Sci., 22, 449 (1956).

43. A. L. Kimball, Jr., General Electric Rev., 27, 244 (1924).

44. B. Maxwell, ASTM Bull., #215, 76 (July, 1956).

45. A. N. Gent, British J. Appl. Phys., 11, 165 (1960).

46. H. Roelig, Rubber Chem. Techn., 18, 62 (1945).

47. C. S. Wilkinson and S. D. Gehman, Anal. Chem., 22, 283 (1950).

48. N. M. Trivisonno, C. A. Stearns, and J. M. Kline, Rubber Chem. Techn., 35, 937 (1962).

49. R. S. Marvin, E. R. Fitzgerald and J. D. Ferry, J. Appl. Phys., 21, 197 (1950).

50. H. Markovitz, P. Yavorsky, R. Harper, L. Zapas, and T. DeWitt, Rev. Sci. Instr., 23, 430 (1952).

51. D. O. Miles, J. Appl. Phys., 33, 1422 (1962).

52. M. H. Birnboim and J. D. Ferry, J. Appl. Phys., 32, 2305 (1961).

53. C. W. Painter, ASTM Bull., #177, 45 (Oct. 1951).

54. S. D. Gehman, Rubber Chem. Techn., 30, 1202 (1957).

55. P. Lord and R. E. Wetton, J. Sci. Instr., 38, 385 (1961).

56. W. Philippoff, J. Appl. Phys. 24, 685 (1953).

57. J. Koppelmann, Rheol. Acta, 1, 20 (1958).

58. R. N. Shroff, D. I. Livingston, and G. S. Fielding-Russell, Rubber Chem. Techn., 43, 1491 (1970).

59. E. Fukada and M. Date, J. Japan. Soc. Test. Matr., 10, 344 (1961).

60. M. Yoshino and M. Takayanagi, J. Japan. Soc. Test. Matr., 8, 330 (April 1959).

61. W. P. Mason and H. J. McSkimin, <u>Bell Syst. Tech. J.</u>, 31, #1,
     121 (1952).

62. H. A. Waterman, <u>Kolloid Zeit.</u>, 192, 1 and 9 (1963).

63. B. A. Dunell and J. H. Dillon, <u>Textile Res. J.</u>, 21, 393 (1951).

64. B. E. Read, <u>Proc. 5th Inter. Congr. Rheology</u>, Vol. 4,
     S. Onogi, Ed., Univ. Tokyo Press, Tokyo, 1970, p. 65.

65. J-F. Jansson, <u>Polymer Systems, Deformation and Flow,</u>
     R. E. Wetton and R. W. Whorlow, Ed., Macmillan, London,
     p. 85, 1968.

66. M. L. Williams, R. F. Landel, and J. D. Ferry, <u>J. Am. Chem.
     Soc.</u>, 77, 3701 (1955).

67. M. L. Williams, J. D. Ferry, <u>J. Coll. Sci.</u>, 9, 479 (1954).

68. K. Ninomiya and J. D. Ferry, <u>J. Colloid Sci.</u>, 14, 36 (1959).

69. L. C. E. Struik and F. R. Schwarzl, <u>Rheol. Acta</u>, 8, 134 (1969).

70. F. R. Schwarzl, <u>Rheol. Acta</u>, 9, 382 (1970).

71. F. R. Schwarzl, <u>Rheol. Acta</u>, 10, 165 (1971).

72. P. Nutting, <u>Proc. Am. Soc. Testing Mater.</u>, 21, 1162 (1921).

73. R. Buchdahl and L. E. Nielsen, <u>J. Appl. Phys.</u>, 22,1344 (1951).

74. H. Leaderman, <u>J. Appl. Mech.</u>, 6, A79 (1939).

75. B. A. Dunell and A. V. Tobolsky, <u>J. Chem. Phys.</u>, 17, 1001
     (1949).

76. B. A. Dunell and A. V. Tobolsky, <u>Textile Res. J.</u>, 19, 631
     (1949).

77. W. P. Cox and E. H. Merz, <u>J. Polymer Sci.</u>, 28, 619 (1958).

78. W. P. Cox and E. H. Merz, <u>ASTM Spec. Tech. Publ.</u>, No. 247,
     Am. Soc. Testing Materials, Philadelphia, Pa. p. 178, 1958.

79. J. R. Van Wazer, J. W. Lyons, K. Y. Kim, and R. E. Colwell,
     <u>Viscosity and Flow Measurements: A Laboratory Handbook of
     Rheology</u>, Interscience, New York, 1963.

80. T. W. DeWitt, <u>J. Appl. Phys.</u>, 26, 889 (1955).

81. S. Onogi, T. Masuda, and T. Ibaragi, <u>Kolloid Zeit.</u>, 222,
     110 (1968).

82. S. Onogi, T. Fujii, H. Kato, and S. Ogihara, <u>J. Phys. Chem.</u>,
     68, 1598 (1964).

83. B. J. Lazan, <u>Modern Plast.</u>, 20, 83 (Nov. 1942).

84. B. J. Lazan and A. Yorgiadis, <u>Modern Plast.</u>, 21, 119
     (Aug. 1944).

85. S. D. Gehman, P. J. Jones, and D. E. Woodford, <u>Ind. Eng. Chem.</u>
     35, 964 (1943).

86. K. E. Guir, C. S. Wilkinson, Jr., and S. D. Gehman,
     <u>Ind. Eng. Chem.</u>, 44, 720 (1952).

87. B. Maxwell, <u>J. Polymer Sci.</u>, 20, 551 (1956).

88. A. R. Payne, <u>J. Appl. Polymer Sci.</u>, 6, 57 (1962), 7, 873 (1963),
     and 9, 2273 (1965).

89. A. R. Payne and W. F. Watson, <u>Rubber Chem. Techn.</u>, 36, 147
     (1963).

90. A. M. Gessler and A. R. Payne, <u>J. Appl. Polymer Sci.</u>, 7,
     1815 (1963).

91. J. M. Lifshitz and A. Rotem, <u>J. Composite Mater.</u>, 3, 412 (1969).

92. B. Maxwell and J. E. Heider, <u>Trans. SPE</u>, 2, 174 (1962).

93. B. Maxwell and C. Guimon, <u>J. Appl. Polymer Sci.</u>, 6, 83 (1962).

94. G. E. Warnaka and H. T. Miller, <u>Rubber Chem. Techn.</u>, 39,
     1421 and 1428 (1966).

95. A. H. Lepie, <u>Rev. Sci. Instr.</u>, 40, 1004 (1969).

96. J. A. Sauer and W. J. Oliphant, <u>Proc. ASTM</u>, 49, 1119 (1949).

97. M. G. Sharma and J. K. Sen, <u>J. Appl. Polymer Sci.</u>, 9, 561
     (1965).

98. R. Clamroth, <u>Kolloid Zeit.</u>, 177, 116 (1961).

99. L. E. Nielsen, Unpublished data, Monsanto Co.

100. N. H. Canter, <u>J. Polymer Sci.</u>, A2, 6, 155 (1968).

101. P. Mason, J. Appl. Polymer Sci., 4, 212 (1960).

102. P. Mason, J. Appl. Polymer Sci., 5, 428 (1961).

103. K. W. Hillier and H. Kolsky, Proc. Phys. Soc., A62, 111 (1949).

104. K. W. Hillier, Trans. Inst. Rubber Ind., 26, 64 (1950).

105. P. Mason, Physical Properties of Polymers, SCI Monograph
      No. 5, Macmillan, London, 1959, p. 262.

106. P. Mason, J. Appl. Polymer Sci., 1, 63 (1959).

107. H. G. Weyland, Textile Res. J., 31, 629 (1961).

108. R. W. Lawton and A. L. King, J. Appl. Phys., 22, 1340 (1951).

109. L. E. Nielsen and R. Buchdahl. J. Appl. Phys., 21, 488 (1950).

110. A. J. Kovacs, R. A. Stratton, and J. D. Ferry, J. Phys. Chem.,
      67,152 (1963).

111. J. E. Eldridge, J. Appl. Polymer Sci., 11, 1199 (1967).

112. V. E. Malpass, Appl. Polymer Symp., No. 12, 267 (1969).

113. A. S. Kenyon and L. E. Nielsen, J. Macromol. Sci., A3,
      275 (1969).

114. W. Wrasidlo, J. Polymer Sci., A2, 9, 1603 (1971).

115. L. E. Nielsen, J. Appl. Phys., 25, 1209 (1954).

116. W. Stockmair, Kunststoffe, 52, 593 (1962).

117. H. A. Flocke, Kolloid Zeit., 180, 118 (1962).

118. E. Passaglia, SPE Trans., 4, 169 (1964).

119. N. G. McCrum, J. Polymer Sci., B2, 495 (1964).

120. S. G. Turley and H. Keskkula, J. Appl. Polymer Sci., 9,
      2693 (1965).

121. S. Onogi, Y. Fukui, T. Asada, and Y. Naganuma, Proc. 5th
      Internat. Congr. Rheology, Vol. 4, S. Onogi, Ed., Univ. Tokyo,
      1970, p. 87.

122. H. Jacobs and E. Jenckel, Makromol. Chem., 43, 132 (1961).

123. K. H. Illers and H. Breuer, J. Colloid Sci., 18, 1 (1963).

124. J. H. Dumbleton and T. Murayama, Kolloid Zeit., 220,
      41 (1967).

125. S. Newman and W. P. Cox, *J. Polymer Sci.*, 46, 29 (1960).

126. D. W. Woods, *Nature,* 174, 753 (1954).

127. R. L. Miller, *Polymer*, 1, 135 (1960).

128. G. V. Vinogradov, E. A. Dzyura, A. Ya. Malkin, and
      V.A. Grechanovskii, *J. Polymer Sci.*, A2, 9, 1153 (1971).

129. W. P. Cox, R. A. Isaksen, and E. H. Merz, *J. Polymer Sci.*,
      44, 149 (1960).

130. H. Hoegberg, S. E. Lovell, and J. D. Ferry, *Acta Chem. Scand.*,
      14, 1424 (1960).

131. T. P. Yin, S. E. Lovell, and J. D. Ferry, *J. Phys. Chem.*,
      65, 534 (1961).

132. Y. Oyanogi and J. D. Ferry, *Proc. 4th Internat. Congr.
      Rheology*, Part 2, E. H. Lee, Ed., Wiley, New York, p. 491,
      1965.

133. G. Pezzin, G. Ajroldi, and C. Garbuglio, *Rheol. Acta*,
      8, 304 (1969).

134. R. Marvin, *Viscoelasticity: Phenomenological Aspects*,
      Chap. 2, J. T. Bergen, Ed., Academic Press, New York, 1960.

135. T. Masuda, K. Kitagawa, and S. Onogi, *Polymer J.*, 1,
      418 (1970).

136. N. R. Langley, *Macromol.*, 1, 348 (1968).

137. N. R. Langley and J. D. Ferry, *Macromol.*, 1, 353 (1968).

138. E. Jenckel, *Kolloid Zeit.*, 136, 142 (1954).

139. L. E. Nielsen, *J. Appl. Polymer Sci.*, 8, 511 (1964).

140. T. Murayama and J. P. Bell, *J. Polymer Sci.*, A2, 8, 437
      (1970).

141. P. J. Flory, *Principles of Polymer Chemistry*, Cornell Univ.
      Press, Ithaca, N.Y., 1953.

142. L. R. G. Treloar, *Physics of Rubber Elasticity*, 2nd Ed.,
      Clarendon Press, Oxford, 1958.

143. F. Bueche, Physical Properties of Polymers, Interscience,
      New York, 1962.

144. A. V. Tobolsky, Properties and Structure of Polymers,
      John Wiley and Sons, New York, 1960.

145. D. Katz and G. Salee, J. Polymer Sci., A2, 6, 801 (1968).

146. L. E. Nielsen, J. Macromol. Sci., C3, 69 (1969).

147. M. F. Drumm, C. W. H. Dodge, and L. E. Nielsen, Ind. Eng.
      Chem., 48, 76 (1956).

148. K. Ueberreiter and G. Kanig, J. Chem. Phys., 18, 399 (1950).

149. G. Lottanti and R. Simeoni, Kunststoffe, 59, 357 (1959).

150. D. E. Kline, J. Polymer Sci., 47, 237 (1960).

151. H. D. Heinze, K. Schmieder, G. Schnell, and K. A. Wolf,
      Rubber Chem. Techn., 35, 776 (1962); Kautschuk Gummi, 14,
      208 (1961).

152. P. Mason, Polymer, 5, 625 (1964).

153. K. Shibayama and Y. Suzuki, J. Polymer Sci., A3, 2637
      (1965).

154. K. Shibayama and Y. Suzuki, Rubber Chem. Techn., 40,
      476 (1967).

155. G. Pohl and S. Kästner, J. Polymer Sci., C16, 4133 (1968).

156. K. Shibayama, T. Tanaka, and D. H. Solomon, J. Macromol. Sci.,
      A1, 1531 (1967).

157. R. E. Cuthrell, J. Appl. Polymer Sci., 11, 949 (1967).

158. D. H. Solomon, B. C. Loft, and J. D. Swift, J. Appl. Polymer
      Sci., 11, 1593 (1967).

159. L. E. Nielsen, J. Appl. Polymer Sci., 2, 351 (1959).

160. K. Okano, Repts. on Progress in Polymer Phys. In Japan, 4,
      31 (1961).

161. I. Uematsu and Y. Uematsu, J. Japan. Soc. Testing Mater.,
      10, 388 (1961); Rheol. Abst., 4, #4, 15 (1961).

162. P. J. Flory, Trans. Faraday Soc., 51, 848 (1955).

163. F. Bueche, J. Polymer Sci., 22, 113 (1956).

164. A. V. Tobolsky, J. Chem. Phys., 37, 1139 (1962).

165. A. V. Tobolsky and V. D. Gupta, Textile Res. J., 33, 761 (1963).

166. L. E. Nielsen and F. D. Stockton, J. Polymer Sci., A1, 1995 (1963).

167. W. R. Krigbaum, R. J. Roe, and K. J. Smith, Jr., Polymer, 5, 533 (1964).

168. A. Bondi, J. Polymer Sci., A2, 5, 83 (1967).

169. J. C. Halpin and J. L. Kardos, J. Appl. Phys., 43, 2235 (1972).

170. R. W. Gray and N. G. McCrum, J. Polymer Sci., A2, 7, 1329 (1969).

171. A. E. Woodward, J. A. Sauer, and R. A. Wall, J. Polymer Sci., 50, 117 (1961).

172. R. F. Boyer, Polymer Eng. Sci., 8, 161 (1968).

173. A. E. Woodward and J. A. Sauer, Adv. Polymer Sci., 1, 114 (1958).

174. J. A. Sauer and R. G. Saba, J. Macromol. Sci., A3, 1217 (1969).

175. J. A. Sauer, J. Polymer Sci., C32, 69 (1970).

176. Y. S. Papir and E. Baer, Mater. Sci. Eng., 8, 310 (1971).

177. N. G. McCrum, B. E. Read, and G. Williams, Anelastic and Dielectric Effects in Polymeric Solids, Wiley, New York, 1967.

178. N. G. McCrum, J. Polymer Sci., 54, 561 (1961).

179. L. E. Nielsen, J. Polymer Sci., 42, 357 (1960).

180. S. Matsuoka, Polymer Eng. Sci., 5, 142 (1965).

181. T. Fujiki, M. Saito, M. Uemura, and Y. Kosaka, J. Polymer
      Sci., A2, 8, 153 (1970).

182. K. Tsuge, H. Enjoji, H. Terada, Y. Ozawa, and Y. Wada,
      Jap. J. Appl. Phys., 1, 270 (1962).

183. K. M. Sinnott, J. Polymer Sci., B3, 945 (1965).

184. K. Schmieder and K. Wolf, Kolloid Zeit., 134, 149 (1953).

185. M. Takayanagi, Memoirs Faculty Eng. Kyushu Univ., 23, #1, 1
      (1963).

186. W. J. MacKnight, L. W. McKenna, and B. E. Read, J. Appl.
      Phys., 38, 4208 (1967).

187. Z. H. Stachurski and I. M. Ward, J. Macromol. Sci., B3,
      427, 445 (1969).

188. C. A. F. Tuijnman, Polymer, 4, 259 (1963).

189. K. M. Sinnott, J. Appl. Phys., 37, 3385 (1966).

190. R. C. Rempel, A. E. Weaver, R. H. Sands, and R. L. Miller,
      J. Appl. Phys., 28, 1082 (1957).

191. T. K. Kwei, H. Schonhorn, and H. L. Frisch, J. Appl. Phys.,
      38, 2512 (1967).

192. D. R. Fitchmun and S. Newman, J. Polymer Sci., A2, 8,
      1545 (1970).

193. H. M. Zupko, Macromol., 4, 761 (1971).

194. H. L. Frisch, H. Schonhorn, and T. K. Kwei, Elastoplast.,
      3, 214 (1971).

195. L. E. Nielsen, R. Buchdahl, and R. Levreault, J. Appl. Phys.,
      21, 607 (1950).

196. K. Wolf, Kunststoffe, 41, 89 (1951).

197. L. E. Nielsen, J. Amer. Chem. Soc., 75, 1435 (1953).

198. F. Kollinsky and G. Markert, Adv. Chem. Series, 99, 175
      (1971).

199. G. Kraus and K. W. Rollman, Adv. Chem. Series, 99, 189 (1971).

200. A. Dobry and F. Boyer-Kawenoki, J. Polymer Sci., 2, 90 (1947).

201. L. E. Nielsen and S. N. Chinai, in L. E. Nielsen, Mechanical Properties of Polymers, Van Nostrand Reinhold, New York, 1962, p. 173.

202. G. King, J. Colloid Sci., 2, 551 (1947).

203. G. W. Becker and H. Oberst, Kolloid Zeit., 152, 1 (1957).

204. K. H. Illers, Makromol. Chem., 38, 168 (1960).

205. A. E. Woodward, J. A. Sauer, C. W. Deeley, and D. E. Kline, J. Colloid Sci., 12, 363 (1957).

206. A. E. Woodward, J. M. Crissman, and J. A. Sauer, J. Polymer Sci., 44, 23 (1960).

207. J. B. Jackson, Polymer, 10, 159 (1969).

208. G. A. Gordon, J. Polymer Sci., A2, 9, 1693 (1971).

209. J. Kurz and J. Woodbrey, unpublished data, Monsanto Co.

210. I. Yannas, Science, 160, 298 (1968).

211. D. H. Rasmussen and A. P. MacKenzie, J. Phys. Chem., 75, 967 (1971).

212. J. Janacek and J. Kolarik, J. Polymer Sci., C16, 279, 441 (1967).

213. J. Janacek, J. Polymer Sci., C23, 373 (1968).

214. M. Baccaredda, E. Butta, V. Frosini, and S. de Petris, J. Polymer Sci., A2, 5, 1296 (1967).

215. K. H. Illers and E. Jenckel, Rheol. Acta, 1, 322 (1958).

216. M. C. Shen and J. D. Strong, J. Appl. Phys., 38, 4197 (1967).

217. M. C. Shen, J. D. Strong, and H. Schlein, J. Macromol. Sci., A3, 1315 (1969).

218. M. C. Shen and E. H. Cirlin, J. Macromol. Sci., B4, 293 (1970).

219. R. J. Morgan and L. E. Nielsen, J. Polymer Sci., A2, 10, 1575 (1972).

220. J. Janacek and J. D. Ferry, *J. Macromol. Sci.*, B5, 219 (1971).

221. J. Kolarik and J. Janacek, *J. Polymer Sci.*, A2, 10, 11 (1972).

222. T. Kawaguchi, *J. Polymer Sci.*, 32, 417 (1958).

223. K. H. Illers, *Physics of Non-Crystalline Solids*, J. A. Prins, Ed., North Holland, Amsterdam, 1965, p. 320.

224. W. J. Jackson, Jr. and J. R. Caldwell, *Adv. Chem. Series*, 48, 185 (1965).

225. W. J. Jackson, Jr. and J. R. Caldwell, *J. Appl. Polymer Sci.*, 11, 211, 227 (1967).

226. L. M. Robeson and J. A. Faucher, *J. Polymer Sci.*, B7, 35 (1969).

227. L. M. Robeson, *Polymer Eng. Sci.*, 9, 277 (1969).

228. L. Bohn, *Kunststoffe*, 53, 826 (1963).

229. G. Pezzin, *J. Appl. Polymer Sci.*, 11, 2553 (1967).

230. K. Nakamura, F. Hashimoto, M. Nakanishi, N. Kinjo, T. Komatsu, and T. Nakagawa, *Proc. 5th Internat. Congr. Rheol.*, S. Onogi, Ed., Univ. Tokyo Press, Tokyo, 1970, Vol. 3, p. 409.

231. Y. Chae, *J. Paint Techn.*, 38, 285 (1966).

232. G. Adams and J. H. Gibbs, *J. Chem. Phys.*, 43, 139 (1965).

233. R. S. Stearns, I. N. Duling, and R. H. Johnson, *Ind. Eng. Chem.* (Prod. Res. Dev.), 5, 306 (1966).

234. G. P. Johari and M. Goldstein, *J. Chem. Phys.*, 53, 2372 (1970).

235. G. Raumann and D. W. Saunders, *Proc. Phys. Soc.*, 77, 1028 (1961) and 79, 1221 (1962).

236. K. H. Hellwege, R. Kaiser, and K. Kuphal, *Kolloid Zeit.*, 157, 27 (1958).

237. I. M. Ward, J. Macromol. Sci., B1, 667 (1967).

238. Z. H. Stachurski and I. M. Ward, J. Polymer Sci., A2, 6,
      1083 (1968).

239. C. D. Armeniades and E. Baer, J. Polymer Sci., A2, 9,
      1345 (1971).

240. R. F. Hearmon, Introduction to Applied Anisotropic Elasticity,
      Oxford Univ., 1961.

241. S. A. Ambartsumyan, Theory of Anisotropic Plates, Technomic,
      Stamford, Conn., 1970.

242. J. E. Ashton and J. M. Whitney, Theory of Laminated
      Plates, Technomic, Stamford, Conn., 1970.

243. R. D. Andrews, J. Appl. Phys., 25, 1223 (1954).

244. J. Spence, J. Phys. Chem., 43, 865 (1939).

245. R. S. Stein, J. Polymer Sci., 24, 383 (1957).

246. R. S. Stein and A. V. Tobolsky, Textile Res. J., 18, 201
      (1948).

247. D. W. Saunders, Trans. Faraday Soc., 52, 1414 (1956)
      and 53, 860 (1957).

248. D. I. Livingston and J. E. Brown, Jr., Proc. 5th Internat.
      Congr. Rheol., Vol. 4, S. Onogi, Ed., Univ. Tokyo Press,
      Tokyo, 1970, p. 25.

249. Z. W. Wilchinsky, Encyclopedia of Pol. Sci. Techn., Vol. 9,
      Interscience, New York, 1968, p. 624.

250. A. Elliott, E. J. Ambrose, and R. B. Temple, J. Chem. Phys.,
      16, 877 (1948).

251. R. S. Stein and F. H. Norris, J. Polymer Sci., 21, 381 (1956).

252. R. J. Samuels, J. Polymer Sci., A3, 1741 (1965).

253. F. P. Chappel, Polymer, 1, 409 (1960).

254. D. Patterson and I. M. Ward, Trans. Faraday Soc., 53, 1516
      (1957).

255. C. R. Desper and R. S. Stein, J. Appl. Phys., 37, 3990 (1966).

256. A. B. Thompson and D. W. Woods, Trans. Faraday Soc., 52, 1383 (1956).

257. W. H. Charch and W. W. Moseley, Jr., Textile Res. J., 29, 525 (1959).

258. W. W. Moseley, Jr., J. Appl. Polymer Sci., 3, 266 (1960).

259. H. M. Morgan, Textile Res. J., 32, 866 (1962).

260. R. E. Robertson and R. J. Buenker, J. Polymer Sci., A2, 4889 (1964).

261. J. Hennig, Kolloid Zeit, 200, 46 (1964).

262. H. A. Waterman, Kolloid Zeit., 196, 18 (1964).

263. J. H. Dumbleton, J. Polymer Sci., A2, 6, 795 (1968).

264. M. Takayanagi, K. Imada, and T. Kajiyama, J. Polymer Sci., C15, 263 (1966).

265. L. Holliday and J. W. White, Pure and Appl. Chem., 26, #3-4, 545 (1971).

266. M. Takano and L. E. Nielsen, Unpublished data, Monsanto Co.

267. V. Frosini and A. E. Woodward, J. Polymer Sci., A2, 7, 525, (1969).

268. C. D. Armeniades, E. Baer, and J. K. Rieke, J. Appl. Polymer Sci., 14, 2635 (1970).

269. M. W. Darlington and D. W. Saunders, J. Macromol. Sci., B5, 207 (1971).

270. A. Mueller, Proc. Royal Soc., A138, 514 (1932).

271. E. R. Andrew, J. Chem. Phys., 18, 607 (1950).

272. S. Okajima and A. Takeuchi, J. Polymer Sci., A2, 5, 1317 (1967).

273. J. H. Daane and S. Matsuoka, Polymer Eng. Sci., 8, 246 (1968).

274. K. H. Hellwege, R. Kaiser, and K. Kuphal, Kolloid Zeit.,
      147, 155 (1956).

275. Z. H. Stachurski and I. M. Ward, J. Polymer Sci., A2, 6,
      1817 (1968).

276. I. M. Ward, Polymer Systems, Deformation and Flow,
      R. E. Wetton and R. W. Whorlow, Ed., Macmillan, London,
      1968, p. 1.

277. H. Wright, C. S. N. Faraday, E. F. T. White, and
      L. R. G. Treloar, J. Phys., D4, 2002 (1971).

278. G. R. Davies, A. J. Owen, I. M. Ward, and V. D. Gupta,
      J. Macromol. Sci., B6, 215 (1972).

279. N. H. Ladizesky and I. M. Ward, J. Macromol. Sci., B5,
      745 (1971).

280. N. Shito and M. Sato, J. Polymer Sci., C16, 1069 (1967).

281. J. Brandrup and E. H. Immergut, Polymer Handbook, Interscience,
      New York, 1966.

282. W. E. Fitzgerald and L. E. Nielsen, Proc. Royal Soc., A282,
      137 (1964).

283. J. E. Fields and L. E. Nielsen, J. Appl. Polymer Sci., 12,
      1041 (1968).

284. L. E. Nielsen, Polymer Eng. Sci., 9, 356 (1969).

285. A. Eisenberg, H. Matsura, and T. Yokoyama, J. Polymer Sci.,
      A2, 9, 2131 (1971).

286. T. Miyamoto, K. Kodama, and K. Shibayama, J. Polymer Sci.,
      A2, 8, 2095 (1970).

287. R. Buchdahl and L. E. Nielsen, J. Appl. Phys., 21, 482 (1950).

288. L. E. Nielsen, Appl. Polymer Symposia, No. 12, 249 (1969).

289. S. Miyata and T. Hata, Proc. 5th Internat. Congr. Rheol.
      Vol. 3, S. Onogi, Ed., Univ. Tokyo Press, Tokyo, 1970, p. 71.

290. E. B. Atkinson and R. F. Eagling, Physical Properties of
      Polymers, Soc. Chem. Ind. Monograph #5, 1959, p. 197.

291. R. Buchdahl and L. E. Nielsen, J. Polymer Sci., 15, 1 (1955).

292. E. Jenckel and H. U. Herwig, Kolloid Zeit., 148, 57 (1956).

293. R. Ecker, Rubber Chem. Techn., 30, 200 (1957).

294. Y. Takahashi, J. Appl. Polymer Sci., 5, 468 (1961).

295. A. D. McIntyre, J. Appl. Polymer Sci., 7, 1291 (1963).

296. K. Fujino, Y. Ogawa, and H. Kawai, J. Appl. Polymer Sci.,
      8, 2147 (1964).

297. K. Fujimoto and N. Yoshimura, Rubber Chem. Techn., 41,
      1109 (1968).

298. P. Zitek and J. Zelinger, J. Polym. Sci., A1, 6, 467 (1968).

299. M. Matsuo, C. Nozaki, and Y. Iyo, Polymer Eng. Sci., 9,
      197 (1969).

300. G. Kraus, K. W. Rollman, and J. T. Gruver, Macromol., 3,
      92 (1970).

301. P. Bauer, J. Hennig, and G. Schreyer, Ang. Makromol. Chem.,
      11, 145 (1970).

302. J. A. Blanchette and L. E. Nielsen, J. Polymer Sci., 20,
      317 (1956).

303. Y. Shinohara, J. Appl. Polymer Sci., 1, 251 (1959).

304. T. T. Jones, British Plast., 33, 525 (1960).

305. H. Tanaka and A. Matsumoto, Repts. Prog. Polymer Phys. Japan,
      5, 151 (1962).

306. W. Albert, Kunststoffe, 53, 86 (1963).

307. M. Buccaredda, E. Butta, and V. Frosini, J. Polymer Sci.,
      C4, 605 (1964).

308. M. Matsuo, T. K. Kwei, D. Klempner, and H. L. Frisch,
      Polymer Eng. Sci., 10, 327 (1970).

309. H. Keskkula, S. G. Turley, and R. F. Boyer, J. Appl. Polymer Sci., 15, 351 (1971).

310. M. Baer, J. Polymer Sci., A2, 417 (1964).

311. E. Perry, J. Appl. Polymer Sci., 8, 2605 (1964).

312. R. J. Angelo, R. M. Ikeda, and M. L. Wallach, Polymer, 6, 141 (1965).

313. J. F. Beecher, L. Marker, R. D. Bradford, and S. L. Aggarwal, J. Polymer Sci., C26, 117 (1969).

314. G. M. Estes, S. L. Cooper, and A. V. Tobolsky, J. Macromol. Sci., C4, 313 (1970).

315. D. H. Kaelble, Trans. Soc. Rheol., 15, 235 (1971).

316. G. Holden, E. T. Bishop, and N. R. Legge, J. Polymer Sci., C26, 37 (1969).

317. G. Cigna, J. Appl. Polymer Sci., 14, 1781 (1970).

318. W. K. Witsiepe, Polymer Preprints, 13, #1, 588 (1972).

319. A. H. Willbourn, Trans. Faraday Soc., 54, 717 (1958).

320. J. Heijboer, Kolloid Zeit., 148, 36 (1956); 171, 7 (1960).

321. J. Heijboer, J.Polymer Sci., C16, 3413 (1968).

322. J. Heijboer, British Plast. J., 1, 3 (1969).

323. J. M. Crissman, J. A. Sauer, and A. E. Woodward, J. Polymer Sci., A2, 5075 (1964).

324. J. A. Sauer and R. G. Saba, Polymers in Space Research, C. L. Segal, M. Shen, and F. N. Kelley, Ed., Marcel Dekker, New York, 1970, p. 181.

325. M. Baccaredda, E. Butta, V. Frosini, and P. L. Magagnini, J. Polymer Sci., A2, 4, 789 (1966).

326. M. Baccaredda, E. Butta, V. Frosini, and S. de Petris, Mater. Sci. Eng., 3, 157 (1968).

327. F. P. Reding, J. A. Faucher, and R. D. Whitman, J. Polymer Sci., 54, S56 (1961).

328. F. R. Dammont and T. K. Kwei, J. Polymer Sci., A2, 5, 761 (1967).

329. W. J. MacKnight and R. J. Tetreault, J. Polymer Sci., C35 117 (1971).

330. R. J. Morgan, L. E. Nielsen, and R. Buchdahl, J. Appl. Phys., 42, 4653 (1971).

331. B. I. Sazhin, T. P. Orlova, and A. M. Lobanov, Polymer Sci USSR, 10, 2228 (1968).

332. R. E. Wetton, G. S. Fielding-Russell, and K. U. Fulcher, J. Polymer Sci., C30, 219 (1970).

333. G. Williams and D. C. Watts, Trans. Faraday Soc., 67 1971 (1971).

334. W. Wrasidlo, Macromol., 4, 642 (1971).

335. J. A. Sauer, R. A. Wall, N. Fuschillo, and A. E. Woodward, J. Appl. Phys., 29, 1385 (1958).

336. B. I. Hunt, J. G. Powles, and A. E. Woodward, Polymer, 5, 323 (1964).

337. J. H. Daane and R. E. Barker, Jr., J. Polymer Sci., B2, 343 (1964).

338. W. J. Schell, R. Simha, and J. J. Aklonis, Polymers in Space Research, C. L. Segal, M. Shen, and F. N. Kelley, Ed., Marcel Dekker, New York, 1970, p. 261.

339. J. Bussink and J. Heijboer, Physics of Non-Crystalline Solids, J. A. Prins, Ed., Interscience, New York, 1965, p. 388.

340. R. J. Morgan, L. E. Nielsen, and R. Buchdahl, In press.

341. R. N. Johnson, A. G. Farnham, R. A. Clendinning, W. F. Hale, and C. N. Merriam, J. Polymer Sci., A1, 5, 2375 (1967).

342. J. Heijboer, J. Polymer Sci., C16, 3755 (1968).

343. K. Deutsch, E. A. W. Hoff, and W. Reddish, J. Polymer Sci., 13, 565 (1954).

344. J. Koppelmann, Kolloid Zeit., 164, 31 (1959).

345. J. Koppelmann, Physics of Non-Crystalline Solids, J. A. Prins, Ed., Interscience, New York, 1965, p. 255.

346. M. C. Shen, J. D. Strong, and F. J. Matusik, J. Macromol. Sci., B1, 15 (1967).

347. K. Shibayama, T. Tanaka, and M. Kodama, Proc. 5th Internat. Congr. Rheol., Vol. 3, S. Onogi, Ed., Univ. Tokyo Press, Tokyo, 1970, p. 451.

348. H. Ochiai, H. Shindo, and H. Yamamura, J. Polymer Sci., A2 9, 431 (1971).

349. J. Janacek and A. Zahradnikova, J. Polymer Sci., A2, 6, 1810 (1968).

350. E. A. W. Hoff, D. W. Robinson, and A. H. Willbourn, J. Polymer Sci., 18, 161 (1955).

351. J. Heijboer, Physics of Non-Crystalline Solids, J. A. Prins, Ed., Interscience, New York, 1965, p. 231.

352. J. A. Sauer and D. E. Kline, J. Polymer Sci., 18, 491 (1955).

353. M. Baccaredda, E. Butta, and V. Frosini, J. Polymer Sci., B3, 189 (1965).

354. O. Yano and Y. Wada, J. Polymer Sci., A2, 9, 669 (1971).

355. C. I. Chung and J. A. Sauer, J. Polymer Sci., A2, 9, 1097 (1971).

356. R. J. Morgan, L. E. Nielsen, and R. Buchdahl, J. Polymer Sci., A2, 9, 1915 (1971).

357. R. A. Haldon, W. J. Schell, and R. Simha, J. Macromol. Sci., B1, 759 (1967).

358. T. Kawaguchi, J. Appl. Polymer Sci., 2, 56 (1959).

359. H. A. Flocke, Kunstoffe, 56, 328 (1966).

360. H. A. Flocke, Kolloid Zeit., 188, 114 (1963).

361. T. Kajiyama and W. J. MacKnight, Macromol., 2, 254 (1969).

362. T. F. Schatzki, J. Polymer Sci., 57, 496 (1962).

363. R. F. Boyer, Rubber Chem. Techn., 36, 1303 (1963).

364. W. Pechhold, S. Blasenbrey, and S. Woerner, Kolloid Zeit.,
     189, 14 (1963).

365. R. J. Morgan, L. E. Nielsen, and R. Buchdahl, J. Appl. Phys.,
     42, 4653 (1971).

366. J. Heijboer, Abstracts IUPAC, Leiden, 1970, p. 617.

367. M. Baccaredda, P. L. Magagnini,and P. Giusti, J. Polymer Sci.,
     A2, 9, 1341 (1971).

368. J. Heijboer, L. C. E. Struik, H. A. Waterman, and M. P. van
     Duijkeren, J. Macromol. Sci., B5, 375 (1971).

369. G. Pizzirani and P. L. Magagnini, J. Appl. Polymer Sci., 11
     1173 (1967).

370. J. E. Kurz, J. C. Woodbrey, and M. Ohta, J. Polymer Sci.,
     A2, 8, 1169 (1970).

371. F. P. Reding, J. A. Faucher, and R. D. Whitman, J. Polymer
     Sci., 54, S56 (1961).

372. J. K. Gillham, G. F. Pezdirtz, and L. Epps, Polymers in Space
     Research, C. L. Segal, M. Shen, and F. N. Kelley, Ed.,
     Marcel Dekker, New York, 1970, p. 145.

373. G. Farrow, J. McIntosh, and I. M. Ward, Makromol. Chem.,
     38, 147 (1960).

374. J. Petersen and B. Ranby, Makromol. Chem., 133, 251 (1970).

375. R. M. Fuoss, J. Amer. Chem. Soc., 63, 369, 378 (1941).

376. F. Wuerstlin, Kolloid Zeit., 113, 18 (1949).

377. Y. Ishida, Kolloid Zeit., 168, 29 (1960).

378. R. D. Andrews and T. J. Hammock, J. Polymer Sci., B3, 655
     (1965).

379. L. Brillouin, Wave Propogation in Periodic Structures,
     2nd Ed., Dover, New York, 1953.

380. A. S. Nowick and W. R. Heller, Adv. in Phys., 14, 101 (1965)
     and 16, 1 (1967).

381. A. V. Granato and K. Lucke, J. Appl. Phys., 27, 583 (1965).

382. R. P. Gupta, J. Phys. Chem., 66, 1 (1962).

383. J. Russell and R. G. Van Kerpel, J. Polymer Sci., 25,
     77 (1957).

384. S. de Petris, V. Frosini, E. Butta, and M. Baccaredda,
     Makromol. Chem., 109, 54 (1967).

385. A. Eisenberg and B. Cayrol, J. Polymer Sci., C35, 129 (1971).

386. A. E. Woodward, J. A. Sauer, and R. A. Wall, J. Chem. Phys.
     30, 854 (1959).

387. Y. Ishida, M. Matsuo, H. Ito, M. Yoshino, F. Irie, and
     M. Takayanagi, Kolloid Zeit., 174, 162 (1961).

388. G. Allen, C. Booth, S. J. Hurst, C. Price, F. Vernon, and
     R. F. Warren, Polymer, 406, 414 (1967).

389. R. K. Eby and K. M. Sinnott, J. Appl. Phys., 32, 1765 (1961).

390. N. G. McCrum, J. Polymer Sci., 34, 355 (1959).

391. E. F. Cuddihy and J. Moacanin, J. Polymer Sci., A2, 8,
     1627 (1970).

392. C. A. May and F. E. Weir, SPE Trans., 2, 207 (1962).

393. J. K. Gillham, Critical Rev. Macromol. Sci., 1, #1, 83 (1972).